KONRAD GATZ AND GERHARD ACHTERBERG

COLOUR
AND
ARCHITECTURE

ARCHITECTURAL BOOK PUBLISHING CO., NEW YORK, 10022

First English Language Edition, 1967

Made and printed in Germany by J. P. Himmer KG, Augsburg
for the publishers ARCHITECTURAL BOOK PUBLISHING CO., NEW YORK, 10022
Library of Congress Catalog Card Number: 66—27872

© Verlag Georg D. W. Callwey, München, 1966

CONTENTS

1 GENERAL REQUIREMENTS FOR EXTERNAL WALLS

A Fundamental constructional requirements

Technical developments in building have made remarkable progress in recent decades. This is particularly evident in the realm of wall elements: traditional materials, as a result of new processes, are today more effective and, with the assistance of improved methods of working, they are also used more intensively. These developments have brought in their train further applications of other known and tried materials. Simultaneously many new materials have been introduced. Numerous materials have been developed or improved with special reference to the following properties: constructional suitability, inherent stability, and ability to retain heat, resistance to weather or chemicals, visual appearance. Many building methods and work processes, introduced in an effort to rationalize and increase efficiency, have meanwhile proved themselves. As far as the execution of external walls is concerned, however, the technical and physical stipulations have often not been thoroughly thought out, nor has sufficient and appropriate care been taken. These stipulations are those which result from the properties of the materials and their combination, from the nature and site of the buildings, and from the utilization of the accommodation. In fact, various building faults repeatedly come to light, when they could have been avoided by using the new knowledge derived from building research.

The subject of this book is the external appearance of a building. This is closely connected with established construction techniques which in turn are determined by their respective production processes. Thus, we shall briefly show first of all the possible choices of material as well as their requirements and manufacture.

The external walls of a building must above all satisfy the following requirements:

a) They must protect the occupier against injurious external influences, especially the effects of weather (rain, hail, snow and radiation) and also against noise and dust.

b) They must also fulfil more or less static functions in the structure of the building. However, one can diminish or disperse this task by only loading the cross wall or by transmitting these loads to columns. Then the external wall has merely its own weight to bear plus any loading it may have to carry from above.

c) Primarily the external walls must contribute, together with other parts of the building, towards offering the occupiers or users of the relevant building the optimum living conditions, especially with regard to habitability. In those buildings which are exclusively or mainly intended for human habitation, the external walls should, amongst other things, effectively regulate damp and be able to absorb excessive air humidity.

d) Finally, the external walls should give the building a pleasing exterior which relates well to its surroundings.

e) Economic requirements have to be considered at the same time as these technical and architectural ones, although the expense of walling, for example in domestic building, only accounts for 10–15 per cent of the building cost. The time required for walling amounts to as much as 20 per cent of the total constructional time on one building. It is for this reason that efforts are being made, especially in domestic building, to rationalize as far as possible the usual building and finishing of external walls, which generally require a great deal of intensive work. (Thus first considerations are economics and fitness for purpose, whilst the visual effect should be suited to the image of the building. In other words, rationalization results from suitable constructional techniques and work processes.) In tall blocks and industrial buildings, on the other hand, unrealistic maintenance costs often dictate the choice of walling material. From this, it may be deduced that more expensive wall systems do indeed demand a greater production cost than brickwork or concrete with simple protective finishes, whilst on the other hand they require less, or no, expenditure for their maintenance.

To be fair to all these varied requirements, those building materials (singly or in combination) which could be considered for external wall construction or treatments, must demonstrate corresponding characteristics which often seem to contradict each other. For example, if one chose building materials for wall cladding with regard only to architectural, technical, mechanical and weathering qualities, then shockproof, smooth, dirt and water repellent materials would be better than softer and more porous ones. However, the latter provide better thermal insulation than heavy, dense materials and they absorb better the damp from room air. Bearing strength on the one hand and weather protection on the other thus require different and contradictory properties, all of which must, however, be reconciled.

It is also not sufficient for the walls actually to fulfil the above mentioned criteria to produce a building. There must be a guarantee that suitable technical measures and the appropriate choice of materials will meet these requirements during the progressive ageing of the building. So, these materials must be protected and maintained against mechanical stresses (like violent impact or steady pressure) and against physical influences in the building (like precipitation and condensation). At the same time maintenance costs should be as low as possible and the walls, both in their construction and surface treatment, as well preserved as possible.

Single skin external walls

In the execution of external walls, apart from purely architectural viewpoints, there are numerous technical, physical and economic needs to be considered, which especially follow from the characteristics of building materials and their combination.

In traditional brickwork buildings there were and still are no difficulties. A brick wall – almost invariably a monolithic element – fulfils (rendered if necessary) all the named requirements. Such a single skin external wall, inclusive of render and paint, is a unit. Its thickness is generally so determined that it satisfies the requirements for thermal insulation and it is, at the same time, sufficiently load bearing. Even the stipulated weather resistance can be met with unrendered brickwork if a suitable brick is chosen. In traditional building, pre-eminently where wood, bricks and natural stone were used, wall constructions resulted which – according to local conditions – could provide extensive protection against weathering. In the majority of single skin construction methods one must, however, plaster the walls externally[1] or "clad" them in some way in order to achieve adequate weather protection.

The thermal insulation coefficient (see later) of a single skin masonry wall is substantially improved if hollow blocks are used. Even then the stability is still generally sufficient, often capable of taking the load of several complete storeys; thus one achieves a considerable saving in weight. If walls of old-fashioned solid masonry were to bear greater loads, then one would have to increase the wall thickness beyond the extent necessary for thermal and sound insulation, and weather protection. Then it becomes expedient to assign the statical tasks to other materials with greater stability. So one comes to buildings assembled from parts in which a bearing frame (as skeleton construction of steel or reinforced concrete) or a core of high-stress concrete (in mantelbeton[2] exteriors or sandwich walls) take over statical functions. For thermal insulation and as a space limiter only one can use a material which performs only these tasks and, consequently, in proportion is less expensive.

Finally, there are assemblies in which various materials take on separate functions if a higher thermal insulation is required. If one constructed walls of normal bricks to a greater thickness for the sake of higher thermal insulation, then the other efficiency characteristics would also rise, with the increased wall thickness, without this being required. Therefore, in such a case, for the sake of expediency, one would also use a built-up walling system consisting of several elements.

Multi-layered external walls

Multi-layered walls can be divided into two groups. In the first the external cladding is part of the wall construction, as for example in large prefabricated units or in certain mantelbeton[2] constructions. The second group comprises those claddings which are separated from the wall by an air gap. This layer of air should then have some connexion with the external air so that the external shell is absolutely vapour proof. This in turn makes it possible to use weather-resistant, refractory and rainproof materials for protection against weather, materials which because of these characteristics usually show a high resistance to vapour diffusion.

For walls whose cladding meets up directly with the structural core the problems of heat and damp retention of the walls must for the time being be carefully tested. Experience has taught us that an investigation of diffusion phenomena in external walls should be strongly advised whenever the properties of walling materials and their interaction are not sufficiently known. The purpose of such calculations should be, by using an appropriate construction, to guard against the formation of condensation on the inside of the walls which would otherwise result from the condensation of the diffusive vapour. Such condensation could lead to saturation. Thus not only would the thermal insulation be substantially reduced but constructional faults would inevitably follow. As the thermal insulating effect of the building rests in the first instance on the smaller heat conductivity of the entrapped air in the

insulating materials, the thermal insulation must in the nature of things be reduced if water (as precipitation or condensation) penetrates into these materials which will have become completely or partially wet.

It is not sufficient just to consider the physical processes of building when planning, estimating and dimensioning the construction. Even during the construction of a building, erected according to a system appropriate to the building type, even then care must be taken that the estimated assumptions prove to be true.

As with the total wall, so must wall claddings fulfil the stated functions in respect of technical, physical, aesthetic and, by no means least, economic factors. The external skin should first of all protect the wall sufficiently against the effects of weather, i.e. rain, hail, wind, radiation and temperature changes, if the inner wall cannot resist these of its own accord: thus changes of form and saturation, and the consequent diminution of thermal insulation, are avoided. On the other hand, one can accentuate or harmonise by means of the external cladding or surface treatment, and stamp, in architectural terms, both the form and colour of the building.

Special building materials with higher efficiency characteristics

As a result of the increasing need for high blocks and large volume halls (ranging from swimming baths to auditoria), greater demands have been placed on the efficiency characteristics of constructional elements. These characteristics are also conditioned by the tendency towards open planning and peripheral walls with large expanses of glass. Finally, these characteristics are further affected by the use of prefabricated parts. On the whole a development may be traced towards top grade materials with specialised fields of application and towards components assembled from such materials.

The higher valued characteristics with respect to technical quality (static stability, thermal and sound insulation) and greater efficiency (resistance to weather, chemical influences and electrolytic reactions) enable most building materials to satisfy a specific task, or only certain functions of the external wall of a building. On the other hand many new materials incline to smaller masses – if related to the dead weight of the skeleton and the total load of the building. Lesser weights, yet again, simplify transport and erection. Thus from the point of view of frame construction many formerly unknown possibilities offer themselves. The separate functions of building materials and the assembled components not only affect the interior of the construction but often show externally as well; thus variations always suggest themselves for the appearance of a building, regarding its materials, colours and structural form.

Summary of the types of external wall claddings

The wall claddings and surface treatments usual in high blocks can be divided as follows:
a) Protective layers:
Painting a plastic substance hardened on to a synthetic material base

Rendering (with or without surface treatment – i. e. paint)
b) Masonry:
Natural stone
Facing bricks (with or without surface treatment)
Clinker
c) Concrete (with or without surface treatment)
d) Slab elements and preformed elements:

Ceramics	Metals:	Synthetic materials
Asbestos cement	ferrous	Glass
Face textured	and non-ferrous	Timber
precast concrete		

Even buildings of prefabricated components or parts utilize the same external finishes – for example, render, ceramic, concrete and slab-shaped claddings – as are usual in traditional buildings.

B Technical prerequisites

Thermal insulation

The economic heating of living and other rooms where human beings spend some time is mainly influenced by the heat retention of the parts of the building enclosing the space. The cost of power and the heating reduces according to the heat insulating efficiency of the walls, ceilings and windows. Next the thermal insulation of the multi-layered walls (prefabricated building elements and light walls of less than 300 kg/m² surface weight) must be especially considered. In the case of walls which are built up from layers arranged parallel to the external surface of the wall, one of these layers usually provides the thermal insulation. The others provide weather protection, take care of load bearing, and form the termination on the room side. The sum of the individual resistances of all the layers yields the total resistance to thermal transmission.

In many prefabricated external wall components, however, the wall is built up, both in cross and longitudinal section, of various materials. That is the case, for example, in walls whose primary structure consists of columns, beams and bracing members whilst the spaces left are filled with insulating materials. For the thermal insulation of such walls the middle value (total thermal transmission figure) of the thermal transmission figures for various building material layers (in accordance with their percentage) is the determining one. This process mainly concerns walls with a surface weight of less than 300 kg/m².

For such components a greater thermal transmission resistance is needed than for heavier walls: e.g. for an external wall with a surface weight of 20 kg/m² in heat retention zone III, a resistance of $1 = 2.60$ m²/h⁰/kcal. On the other hand a heavy wall having otherwise the same dimensions would require $1 = 0.65$ m²/h⁰/kcal. This roughly corresponds to the thermal insulation of a 36.5 cm wide solid-brick wall with a net weight of 1,400 kg/m². External walls for residential buildings with a weight of less than 200 kg/m² must also have double windows or sealed double glazing units. This additional expense arises not only for prefabricated parts but also for all external walls of light weight.

The technically adequate thermal insulation is not always at the same time the most economical one: an additional thermal insulation of the external walls and windows can actually bring about economies in heating costs under certain circumstances, economies which far exceed the higher building costs. Walls of solid bricks show the most favourable relationship between building costs and heating costs when they are 36.5 cm thick with a thermal conductivity of $k = 1.3$. With walls of hollow blocks, being more favourable from the thermotechnical point of view, this optimal relationship for a thickness of 30 cm is a k figure of 1.1. Multi-layer walls achieve this when they have an insulating layer of a thickness of between 5 and 10 cm. The thermal conductivity then amounts to $k = 0.5$ to 0.3.

It is of paramount importance that the thermal insulation of the wall is not reduced through damp penetration either from the external air or from the interior of the room: preventable through the appropriate choice and arrangement of building materials. An increase in damp of one volume per cent raises the thermal conductivity figure by 10–20 per cent.

Renders, paints or "claddings" must prevent the penetration of downpours of rain. However the evaporation rate of the wall to the exterior must not be checked. Basically, those wall elements which are exposed to downpours should be dimensionally thickened to suit the thermal requirements. The same can be said for walls of prefabricated elements. By means of the cladding and the connexion of the individual layers both with each other, with the ceiling and the remaining walls, heat bridges can form. The temperature at these points, especially in the corners of rooms and at panel joints, then lies far below the permissible value. Consequently, diverse temperature differences occur on the inner surface of the wall. In colder places, precipitation occurs and the wall is here completely saturated. Excessive dampness can no longer be compensated for by a plaster intended to form a barrier. With prefabricated concrete elements there is often no control at all of dampness. This can sometimes lead to chronic illness among the occupiers.

Window and wall surfaces: as windows are often planned much larger than is necessary to illuminate the room, or is expedient for the arrangement of furniture, they are often of greater importance for the thermal insulation of the house than the external walls.

If the external area of a room measuring 10 m² has a single window of 2 m², more than half of the thermal loss is a result of this small window area. If the same area of window is in the form of a double window then the thermal loss of the total external wall is reduced by almost 30 per cent. If a 10 m² external surface has a single window of 5 m² then 60 per cent more heat is lost than through the equally large wall area with the 2 m² single window. Double windows reduce the thermal transmission by about half.

The minimum thermal protection for walls, required by climate, can only be achieved through a compound window having three layers of air enclosed by four panes of glass, or through correspondingly built up glass brick walls. Compound windows and sealed double glazing units (see Diagram 5) are certainly more expensive than single windows of the same size and type, but they do offer higher thermal insulation and lower heating costs. In Scandinavian countries this has been recognized and the use of triple windows has become common practice.

Solar gain is appreciable in the winter months on the sunny side of a house, especially if there are south-facing windows. In summer, on the other hand, the sunshine can be troublesome as soon as the panes of glass start to act like radiant heating panels. In such a case, sun shades fixed outside the windows are of help for they are no hindrance whatsoever to winter sunshine, yet afford some protection against summer sunshine. In special cases the use of a glass with a strong reflective quality is helpful.

Thermal storage retention: the total thermal function of an external wall is not only dependent on its resistance to heat transmission to the outside, but also on its ability to store up solar and internal energy which it receives. Correspondingly in winter rooms should be prevented from cooling off too much on account of variable external temperatures or through reduced or temporarily interrupted heating. In summer the heat penetrating from outside should not be allowed to flow through unhindered, otherwise the internal surface of the wall will become excessively warm. A room climate which is as equable as possible should be guaranteed for the occupiers. Finally, with thermal storage, above all in heating systems such as closed stoves which do not run continuously, one should make certain during heating pauses that the inner surface of the wall does not cool off too quickly or too far (i. e. beneath the zero point). This would result in condensation on the wall, penetrating it. Traditional construction of heavy materials with high specific heat fulfils this thermal storage. On the other hand, many new types of construction, especially with multi-layered lightweight walls, cannot adequately store the thermal energy. In other cases, the wall can store heat but the window cannot. A higher standard of window insulation should compensate for the lack of storage capacity, though by this means the storage capacity of the wall as a whole does not improve.

The heat storage capacity is dependent on the weight and average specific heat of a material. The sequence of individual wall layers from inside to outside can also have an effect and should therefore be considered. The number S_{24} marks the thermal storage ability of a material per hour during a 24-hour heating period for every unit of surface at a temperature difference of 1° C. For single skin walls one can determine, with tables, the necessary thermal insulation value which is needed to ensure the desired surface temperature. External walls of light construction require an examination of cooling-off temperatures. For light walls with a weight of 250 kg/m² it is recommended that the "equivalent to brick storage allowance" d_s be calculated. On average, the dividing line between an adequate and an insufficient thermal storage is where there is a "flowing-through time" of 10 hours: this would correspond to a "brick storage equivalent" thickness of 17 cm.

Protection from weather and damp

Together with the thermal technical properties of an external wall, the damp suppression is also an essential determinant in deciding on constructional techniques. Damp can affect the wall from the exterior in the form of downpours (of rain, hail or snow), or can affect the wall from the interior by condensation down the inner surface or within the wall itself; at the same time relative humidity creates a pressure on the wall

if the humidity differs from interior to exterior. Where people are occupying a room, the internal humidity is greater. Therefore condensation moves, in all these cases, from interior to exterior. If the vapour pressure rises above saturation point, dependent on air temperature, then the dampness in the air pours down wall faces in the form of condensed vapour; it saturates the wall and thereby lowers the wall's resistance to thermal transmission. Consequently the external wall must be so built up that the room vapour diffusing through it can be led off to the exterior without causing damage to the wall and without harmfully affecting the inhabitants.

To achieve this there are two possible courses: one can choose porous materials, so that the wall is completely permeable. Alternatively, if one takes materials for the external cladding which are resistant to atmospheric corrosion, are capable of withstanding impact and which always have a high vapour diffusion resistance, then either an internal and correspondingly valued vapour barrier must be fixed or the wall must be double skinned (i. e. of cavity construction). The external skin then only partly contributes to the weather protection, so that precipitations, especially of rain, penetrate the wall. Even in the past, in areas with heavy rainfall, walls were clad with clapboard, slate or roof tiles; also the usual cavity brickwork on the North Sea and Baltic Sea coasts was specifically for this purpose. Present day physical knowledge of building confirms the suitability of such construction. The cavity in such cases is connected to the external air and through convection allows an exchange of air, which diffusion) through joints in the facing material.

The internal damp barrier layer contradicts, however, the demands for an internal wall cladding to occupied rooms, the latter being of vital importance for the room climate. The variable level of humidity in rooms can be balanced by a porous buffer layer between the damp barrier and the room. On the other hand, if the internal wall cladding consists entirely of waterproof materials then the creation of an artificial climate in the rooms is imperative. Thus, whenever in new kinds of buildings the properties of the walling materials and their physical interaction (with multi-layer assembled walls) are not known sufficiently from experience, then in these cases the diffusion phenomena in the external wall should be examined and calculated.

But it is always through the choice of appropriate building materials and of a suitable structure that damp in walls can be prevented from leading to frost damage putrefying symptoms; if this is done, the durability of the wall is ensured, the maintenance costs are kept as low as possible, and the occupiers are guaranteed a healthy room climate.

Rendered buildings are exposed above all on the weather side (in our latitudes this is usually the west) to the effects of precipitation. A downpour of rain with a wind strength of 5 or more (Beaufort) is especially damaging. According to the investigations of the Institute for Materials Science and Testing at the Brunswick Technical High School, render (as opposed to unrendered walls) does offer 9 to 18 times safety against saturation and so extensively protects the wall against the penetration of precipitated water. But the render must be very carefully applied.

With traditional wall thicknesses the penetration of a certain amount of water into the walls was quite harmless. So the render provided the required weather protection. Since the war, however, thin wall techniques have been introduced and have often shown defects as a result of dampness. Today, walling techniques have developed even further, but a minimum thickness of 30 cm is still required. Then, the so-called normal renders are able to prevent the penetration of damp, though in combination with highly porous building materials, as for example porous concretes, these normal renders are usually not sufficient.

Professor Reiher's investigations in Stuttgart have shown that even the kind of sand used for the render can have influence on rain penetration.

It is important that the thermal, dampness and technical properties of the renders are related to the properties of the walling material. Through the application of normal render, render with water-repellent additive, or render with water-repellent coats of paint, the weather-technical properties of a rendered facing can be considerably improved. The numerous traditional, commercial agents in the silicone groups mainly show good results if they amount to 1–3 per cent of the substance; also, the durability and efficiency of the substance can decisively influence the protection against damp. The weather resistance of non-clad or concreted walls is improved through water-repellent paints with which, however, the total exterior of the wall must be treated, completely and evenly. Since paints generally have only a limited life, they must be renewed at intervals. Furthermore it should be noted that most of these materials only become fully effective some weeks after their application.

Film-like coats of lacquer, synthetic emulsions and dispersions bring about good dampness protection. The liquid agents are produced in a special process. They are almost equally suitable for smooth, rough, rendered and unrendered walls. Plastic or hardenable substances on a synthetic basis are also used additionally to coat the external wall.

For the weather protection of prefabricated elements, similar treatments as those described above are also valid in the consideration of constructional-physical processes in the wall. But in this case there ist also the problem of protecting the joints. If the external skin (render, concrete, slab-shaped claddings) has not already been processed in the factory, then the slab face can usually not take a further protective coat. So the joint must be formed in such a way as to resist all weather influences. Some producers of prefabricated wall elements use joint bands approximately in the middle of the wall leaving the external part of the joint open. In other processes, the external side of the joint is closed with a durable plastic substance. In general, good constructional-physical solutions make the assembly more difficult, whilst simple slab faces and simple joints are seldom equal to the stresses of weather and ageing.

Sound Insulation

Noise from lorries, aeroplanes, construction works and so on, increases from year to year. It is felt to be a nuisance and can even cause physical and mental damage to human beings. Therefore sound insulation should be carefully considered when constructing external walls, especially as lightweight walling systems are being used ever more frequently. In traditional heavy walls the window area used to be the place allowing most noise penetration. Nowadays, more noise often penetrates through the walls of a very light construction than through double windows. For prefabricated dwellings (of timber and timber-derived materials), it is therefore recommended that an air noise reduction of no less than -10, up to -20dB, should be used for the external walls. In particular, a room where much time is spent should have a better sound insulation, i. e. at least -3 dB. This can be achieved by means of single skin walls of at least 250 kg/m² and by means of certain multi-layer wall systems.

Fire protection

The problem of external walls today is being increasingly solved by means of either bearing materials or infill panels. Good, light, thermally insulating materials are available for panels, e. g. timber materials or synthetic products. With these lightweight or other easily inflammable materials, special attention must be paid to the fire rating, as in curtain wall construction where the frame is of steel, reinforced concrete or prestressed concrete:

1. External walls with large surface panes of glass: even shortly after the commencement of a fire tensions can occur in glass, when the rise in temperature is slight, which cause it to break. This would immediately cause the fire to spread.
2. External wall slabs of steel: these can lose their shape and firmness in a quite moderate rise in temperature. For the surrounding planes of a room, therefore, such panels can usually only be considered in combination with fire resisting materials.
3. Light metal construction: on account of thermal conductivity and low melting point, such materials are treated here like steel.
4. Stonework: various kinds behave differently in a fire. Thermal expansion and contraction: if cold water should be poured on to hot stones this could easily lead to the destruction of the wall.

It is beyond the scope of this book to examine the combustibility of all building materials and external wall systems. In general, fire prevention regulations should be considered.

C Thermal effect of colour tones

In the colour effect of all architecture, form, colour, light and illumination are closely interrelated. The different aesthetic effects of various colour qualities cannot specifically be discussed here. In the introduction and illustration captions we go into the matter more fully.

The colour not only influences the optimal effect of the building, but often also the construction of external walls: for the choice of materials and their colours, especially cladding panels with joints on south and west façades, the thermal and technological conditions of the cladding must be considered. Using transparent claddings, the material and colour of the backing wall play an important part. Research at the Institute for Technical Physics at Stuttgart has shown that the temperature of a face exposed to sunshine varies considerably according to its colour (see figures 2 and 3). As the temperatures change during the day, considerable stresses can develop in the cladding, causing expansion or contraction of the materials and sometimes leading to costly damage. Thermal stress occurs especially in summer on west façades. A further difficulty is that in the outer skin of the wall are placed materials which have a high surface resistance to heat penetration. This has to be considered especially for panels which are fixed immediately next to a wall. In extreme cases there can be differences in temperature between summer and winter of 100° C. These differences have to be considered in the construction of the wall.

Influence of colour on the surface temperature of external render. West wall (30 cm cellular blocks wall) measured on 5 July 1959 (intensity of rays on a horizontal surface: 660 g cal/cm² per day). The daily repeated changes in temperature lead to periodical changes of stress in the render, and so to damage.
Influence of sun radiation on the temperature of claddings.
Graphical curves of surface temperatures of ceramic tiles of different colours (Association of Ceramic Tile and Other Ceramic Materials Manufacturers) measured on 22 June 1962.

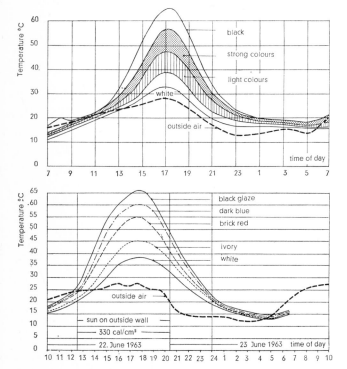

2 MATERIALS AND TECHNIQUES FOR COLOURED EXTERNAL WALLS

A External wall facings of natural stone or marble. Constructional properties of stone

Natural stone as material for walls of inhabited buildings cannot match up to today's demands because of its high weight, thermal conductivity and denseness; its high resistance to damp penetration makes thermal absorption take a very long time. But for plinths, garden walls, landscape architecture and religious buildings, natural stone is still used frequently. The highly weather-resistant natural stones include many naturally attractive colours – from a pure white through yellow, green and red tones to black; this, together with their textures and markings and the variety of surface treatments (rough, smooth or polished), makes natural stone a frequently used external cladding in the form of slabs, strips or mosaic.

These claddings can be fixed to the wall with or without cramps, and either the space is filled with mortar or with strips or dabs of mortar. But today a system without mortar is preferred because of physical advantages (this applies to almost all other claddings as well). Stone panels are also used, in the same manner as other materials, as infill panels within external frames or curtain walls.

Natural stones for external walls have to be weather resistant. Besides this, the stones have not to be materially affected by the stresses of sunlight on the surface, change of temperature and damp. As the stones are not homogeneous materials, but are composed of different minerals, it is difficult to classify them.

Amongst volcanic primeval rocks (consolidation rocks) are those with crystalline structure (granite and variations), very dense rocks (basalt) and rocks out of a dense or glassy matrix with dispersed crystals (porphyry). Through adhesion or connexion by weather, stratified rocks evolve; these include for example limestones, which often are porous. Sandstone is better, the smaller and more homogeneous the grain is. Conglomerate or Puddingstone has a concrete-like character – it is a cemented fragmental rock consisting of rounded fragments of other rocks embedded in a finer matrix. Metamorphic rocks, which originated under pressure, heat or from a chemical reaction, have a slaty, crystalline or glassy structure.

Colour, toughness and weather resistance of natural stone depend on the content of different minerals. Quartz, for example, is transparent or shiny white, very hard and weather resistant; augite is similar, but dark green or black. Feldspar can make the stone gold or brown-red and at the same time less weather-resistant. Pyrites looks golden or variegatedly shining, but it weathers easily and reduces the worth of the stone.

Natural stones normally have a low flexural strength and a varying compressive strength:

Limestones	200 to 1,800 kg/cm²
Sandstones	200 to 3,000 kg/cm²
Consolidation stones	1,400 to 4,000 kg/cm²

In architecture, especially for external claddings, mostly lime-stones are used; one of them is real marble ($CaCO_3$). The stonemason in his treatment of the surfaces, has the following choices – to punch, flatten, bush-hammer, kernel, chisel, smooth, or polish.

Stratified stones, except Quartzite and Gompholite, have good working qualities (for frame saw and mason's work). Different colours and kinds of stone can be used in the construction of external walls. Limestone can easily be polished, but can be eroded by industrial smoke and gases. Therefore polishing cannot be recommended in industrial atmospheres; alternatively one can use smooth stones, sand-blasted stones or stones whose surface is ground to varying degrees, unless polished surfaces are especially wanted for cladding plinths, shop window frames, etc. For porous stones, solutions of linseed oil, wax or paraffin close the pores well. To apply these materials to the stone it should be dry and have a temperature of about 13° C.

In the corrosive air of our towns, especially in areas with high rainfall, dense limestones should be used. Painting with silicon fluoride (Fluatieren) gives a good weather protection to all stones which contain chalk. By such painting, the surfaces of the stones achieve insoluble chemical properties which cannot flake off. If the stones are already weathered the application of silicon fluoride has a damaging rather than beneficial effect.

If sandstones contain a chalky matrix, which can easily be dissolved, the stone decays rapidly. A matrix of clay, on the other hand, makes the stones sensitive to frost. Consolidation stones are normally more difficult to work than stratified stones, but they are very suitable for external claddings in thin slabs (for example, porphyry).

Walls in natural stone

For walls constructed of natural stone, normally the same types of stone are suitable as for external wall cladding. But in this case, besides the attractive exterior, one has to consider strength and the cost. The principal types of wall in natural stone are: random rubble, quarrystone walls, Cyclopean masonry, irregularly coursed walls, regularly coursed walls, semi-worked stones, and ashlar.

Natural stone slabs

Natural stone cladding slabs are mainly 3 to 4 cm thick; using harder stones one can reduce to 2 cm thickness. For the treatment of stone, the Natural Stone Association in Munich has prepared an advisory book, important extracts from which are given below:

Reasonable drawings are the condition for correct application of the stones to the wall: the drawings have to contain all necessary details about cutting the stone, fixing system (type of cramps to be used), independent support of the stones, mortar dabs, jointing and connexion to other parts of the building, and dimensioning and numbering of the individual stones. The wall surface behind the stones has to be prepared by its builder in a way which neither requires breaking away of projections nor excessively large mortar dabs (or needless mortar fill when used behind the whole slab). The wall surface must

not effloresce and not be destructively unstable. The thickness of the layer of mortar must be about 15 to 20 mm, enough to compensate for slight unevenness of the wall or to enable some thicker slabs to be used. On concrete surfaces no shuttering oil should be allowed to remain. Before fixing the slabs the wall below should have been drying out for at least six weeks, in damp periods of the year appropriately longer. Cramps, anchors, and other fixings have to resist corrosion or need to have a protective coating against all chemical influences from the building materials, reagents, or from the atmosphere. Generally it is advisable to use non-rusting metals: if the space behind the slabs is filled up with mortar, galvanised cramps are suitable. They must not be chilled after the galvanising and in no case be worked or shaped (danger of rust). Free standing cramps between slabs of natural stone and wall or insulation layer respectively should consist of chrome nickel steel material number 4571.

Generally, one has to differentiate between cramps with a carrying function and cramps preventing the slabs from falling outwards. For outside facings, wire must never be used for the carrying function, but only cramps with integral dowels or other fixing appliances. The required strength of cramps and their ancillary fixings results from a statical calculation. If the statical calculation shows that distributor discs are necessary, these have to be irremovably fixed to the cramps (welding is suitable).

Normally, cramp dowels may be fixed vertical and flush, horizontal, or according to a given gradient. Gypsum must not be used. This especially concerns the fixing of cramps and carrying devices in the wall. Each slab has to be connected with the wall in a way that allows it all necessary support from the anchorage; cramps have to be in four points to prevent twisting. In every upper floor the fixtures or cramps have to be fixed in a way that makes every upper row of slabs independent from the lower one.

One has to watch that the types of cramps ordered in the working drawings are in fact used. The depth of the cramps in the wall has to be individually decided according to the thickness of the slabs, condition of the wall below (unit weight and loading capacity) and the statical requirements. Cramps should penetrate at least 5 to 6 cm into the concrete or brickwork. For fixing them, good cement mortar with a mixing ratio 1 : 3 is necessary. Cleaning the holes carefully and making them wet guarantees a perfect connexion between mortar and brickwork. The cramps should be set according to the working drawings and the actual condition of the wall in the vertical and horizontal joints and wedged with small stones in the mortar. The remaining section between the hole in the slab and the surface of the slab not be should less than 10 mm. Depending on the height above ground, the surface of the wall below and the stone chosen, different methods of fixing are suitable: the setting of stone slabs on a layer of mortar without anchoring is only possible for small slabs, e. g. narrow shallow natural stone slabs no higher than first floor level. Sufficient adhesion of stone slabs and wall surface is a prime requisite; therefore sometimes a rough cement render is necessary. Fixing slabs on a layer of mortar with additional supports is only feasible for porous stone and stone with sufficient adhesion to the mortar. Leaving an open gap behind the slabs provides ventilation of the façade. This method (without mortar) is used for stone which is especially stable and has bad adhesion to mortar. It is particularly advisable for claddings on a surface consisting of a glued insulation layer. The lowest slab should not sit on the ground but should be hanging free to be able to move under pressure. Horizontal and vertical joints should be 4 mm wide throughout. The joints to window frames, lighting fixtures and advertising signs etc. should be carried out with special care.

Outside walls which are more than one storey high need a horizontal expansion joint at every floor level and a vertical one every 6 to 8 m. (flexible joints). This also applies to continuous vertical or horizontal strips of cladding (columns and continuous upstands). Large surfaces have to be subdivided into independent panels.

All expansion joints should be 1 cm wide and have to be carried out with special care; they have to go through to the surface of the backing wall. Spacers or remaining smudges of mortar should be removed from the expansion joints to prevent any transmission of load. The row of slabs above an expansion joint must under no circumstances load the lower row.

All expansion joints are filled with mastic which is permanently plastic and does not mark the slabs or move excessively (at least 1 cm deep). The space behind can be filled with a suitable soft material which does not rot (for example, glass wool, rock wool or Moltoprene).

Facing narrow shallow slabs of natural stone

Such slabs use the good properties of natural stone in an economic way and achieve attractive effects. Strips are sawn out of slabs of natural stone and split up by special machines in the layers of their stratification. This method gives narrow slabs of a thickness of 15 to 20 mm, a length of 6 to 15 cm and a width of 2 to 4 cm. The visible surfaces have an appearance of fracture, the sides being sawn. In the process of splitting, all pieces which are not solid enough break. Only weather-resistant material from the core is used. The usual colours of the slabs are yellow, grey-brown, white-grey, light grey, dark grey, light and dark green, reddish and black; the varying texture of the stone gives a variety of shades of colour.

The continuous joints can run horizontally or vertically; the slabs can be used for curved surfaces as well. Rough but level lime cement mortar on brickwork or rough cement render on concrete are feasible as undersurface. Dry walls have to be wettened. The mortar consists of washed sand, tufa, cement and chalk mixed in a ratio of 4 : 1/4 : 1/4 : 1.

To shorten the process of hardening, a small portion of genuine high alumina cement can be added. The mortar bed should not be thicker than 1 to 1·5 cm, otherwise there is a risk of "floating". For outside walls more than one storey high, besides the mortar an additional anchoring in the form of 4 to 8 cramps per square metre in necessary.

On high wall surfaces the slabs are fixed above a straight edge in courses from the top downwards; they are pressed into a mortar bed, which is applied with a spatula, so that the horizontal and vertical joints are perfectly filled with mortar. When certain areas have been fixed, mortar which has come out of the joints must be washed down with water and a brush. For outside corners, corner pieces with sides of different length are available to continue the bond around the corner. A later

application of fluorides or wax is unnecessary, even disadvantageous.

Mosaic in natural stone

For mosaic in natural stone – which is more irregular than glass mosaic – primarily basalt, shell-lime, quartzite, slate and marble are used. Except for the marbles (thicknesses 6 to 7 mm, sizes 30/60, 20/60 and 20/40 mm), mosaic in natural stone is not glued on sheets of paper.

The possibilities of aesthetic effect vary according to type of stone, colour and size of stone. The pieces are laid in a bed of hydraulic mortar, i. e. mortar which hardens without air. As hardening component, Roman cement is usually used, and fluorate can be added to prevent efflorescence. The pieces have to be well set, to exclude air voids which might become filled with water (danger of frost). So as not to transmit stresses from the structure to the outer skin, the facing should be subdivided into panels of less than 6 to 10 square metres, their size depending on colour and type of mosaic. Expansion joints have to go through to the brickwork or concrete and have to be filled with suitable sealing material.

B External walls in brick or tile

Bricks vary in colour depending on the clays used and the method of baking – from yellow, red, grey with various nuances to black. The effect can be made even stronger by treating the surface (sanding, roughening) or glazing.

By using different sizes, the appearance of the walls can be made less regular; by staggering the bricks a relief surface can be achieved. More permutations result from different bonds, colour and finish of joints.

In facing brickwork also decorative bonds can be achieved by alternating headers and stretchers, or by inserting some overburnt bricks. A further wide field for using bricks is for infill walls in steel or reinforced concrete frame structures.

Properties and forms of bricks

Outside claddings have to keep out water and the same time allow damp diffusion from inside to the outer surface. Bricks can do this, as the brickwork is able to absorb, and temporarily store, water and to give it off again relatively fast under favourable conditions. This creates the normally very congenial internal climate of brick buildings. The brick can equally distribute the damp, as the capillary system in the construction of the brick is favourable to this process and accelerates it.

One important condition for good weather protection and for avoiding high maintenance costs is the right choice of the bricks and the workmanlike composition of the joint mortar and pointing mortar.

Since the Second World War the brick industry has developed lighter bricks with higher compressive strength. The latter allows one to reduce the thickness of walls. At present there are available facing bricks, engineering bricks and commons in 1½ and 2¼ times normal size and also large cavity bricks. Also, the use of bigger prefabricated brickwall panels is in progress.

Transport of the bricks to the site is now often possible without having to restack them. Many brick manufacturers have almost made transport automatic. The bricks are carried from the stove to the drying place and into the lorries by fork lifts. The difficulty is in adjusting the size of the transportation unit in the factory to the capacity of tower cranes and to organise the transport from the works properly. It is practical to pile the bricks on pallets. The size of the brick stacks has to be appropriate to the hoisting cage of the tower crane; these piles are best held together by iron straps. They can be subdivided into smaller piles of about 180 kg weight; the pallets have an area of 1 : 2 m by 0 : 8 m. It is also possible to bring the bricks in divisible but unbound piles to the site, where they are picked up by the crane with special forks. With these methods, much working time can be saved. Such methods are also of interest to building sites with elevators, as they avoid losses through bricks being broken whilst being roughly offloaded from the delivery lorry. Provided the stacks are the right size, the bricks can be brought to the mason on a special cart, without restacking.

Rationalisation has brought lighter bricks with higher compressive strength, allowing thinner walls, but at the same time this makes the proper construction of facing brickwork more problematic. Previously, external walls were made 38 or 51 cm thick, thus large amounts of water penetrating from outside could be stored pending drying out. Due to their weight they gave a good sound insulation and also good heat insulation. Using thinner walls, these requirements are more difficult to meet. Generally, today's bricks still have the good fundamental qualities of the material. By choosing the right size and quality of brick and the right mortar, structural brickwork can be adapted to the statical requirements, provided the number of openings for windows and doors is not too high.

For the construction of brick walls or brick facings the following principles have to be considered:

Brick is constant in volume. Only the joints can shrink. As the brick contains air pores and holes its heat insulation is good. By special arrangements of the holes and intensified porosity the effect can be further improved. Use of this kind of brick is only possible if they are not load bearing. The heat storage effect can influence the economics of heating.

Properly built brickwork keeps interiors cool in summer and warm in winter. Given a sufficient unit weight of the brickwork the sound insulation is good. But it has to be considered that heavier bricks give less heat insulation than light ones.

Walls of exposed brickwork

Walls are normally built in a bond. By this means, the loads and stresses are equally distributed over the brickwork. The bond of the facing skin determines the appearance. If the facing is able to hold itself up, it need not be interlinked with the backing wall. Brickwork in external walls is used in different forms of construction.

Solid brick walls

Solid exposed brick walls are a wall construction in which the facing is bonded with the backing wall. Therefore in facing and backing wall only the same size of bricks can be used.

Engineering or facing bricks can be used for the facing. Facing bricks have to be solid bricks: they must not contain holes. The wall thickness has to fulfill the requirements of statics and heat insulation. Facing bricks or engineering bricks should have neither cracks nor damaged corners. It is advisable to avoid vertical joints going through facing and backing wall. Three kinds of exposed brick walls may be suggested:

a) Brickwork in normal size bricks. For such brickwork, only bricks with a unit weight of a maximum of 1·4 kg/dm³ should be used. Engineering bricks cannot be used. As headers and stretchers are used alternately, where headers occur penetration of water from a storm is possible. Under permanent stress the storage capacity of this wall is low.

b) Walls 30 cm thick normally are built out of bricks 1½ and 2¼ NF (NF = normal size). Here, no bonds reach through the whole wall. There is always a joint between backing wall and facing. By offsetting the joints of the facing from the ones in the backing wall, continuous vertical joints can be avoided. In regions with heavy rainfall and wind this rule must be adhered to.

c) Walls 36·5 cm thick using DF bricks (DF = narrow deep) have a relatively high percentage of joints. If the wall is built in DF bricks throughout there is a horizontal joint every 5·2 cm. Therefore it is more feasible to build the backing wall in 1½ or 2¼ NF bricks. This avoids a through horizontal joint. There is a continuous joint between the two skins. If this joint is completely filled with mortar it prevents damp penetration.

In solid, exposed, brickwork walls use of 1½ and 2¼ NF bricks increases economy by reducing actual work by 20 per cent. Also, the weather protection is improved, as the number of joints is reduced. For a 24 cm wall, as said before, the header going through is a disadvantage. Sometimes it is possible to use a construction which avoids them. It is possible to work with two skins of stretchers or use 1½ or 2¼ NF bricks and facing shallow bricks. It is questionable whether conditions can be improved by this. If possible, one should avoid 24 cm external walls. For 30 cm walls it seems practical, if one only considers the bond, to use facing or engineering bricks with vertical holes (KHLz) as they are available in 1½ and 2¼ NF sizes. The engineering brick (KMz) and the facing brick (VMz) are only available in DF and NF sizes.

For the choice of sizes, static, heat insulation, quality and storage capacity characteristics of the backing wall have also to be considered. A 36·5 cm is sometimes desirable from aesthetic points of view. But by its high percentage of joints it implies certain disadvantages. It seems also possible to build the wall with 1½ DF bricks, if engineering or facing bricks with vertical holes can be used.

The following table shows the heat insulation of solid exposed brickwork:

Solid brickwork composed of facing and backing walls (no cavity)

Here the outer facing skin and inner backing wall are not a unit, because each skin is built separately. A connexion every fourth course can be done by headers, isolated with bitumen to avoid damp bridges. For this construction the entire wall is built at the same time.

Heat insulation of solid brick walls — heat transmission figures — minimum thickness of walls — heat insulation figures for thickness from 11.5 to 36.5 cm.

Type of wall	Unit weight of brick	Heat transmission figure for brickwork	Minimum thickness of wall (in cm) without plaster or render Load bearing external walls in region			Partition walls and staircase walls	Thermal retention value including 2 cm render, 1.5 cm plaster in wall thicknesses of				
	kg/dm³	kcal/mh⁰	I	II	III	I and II	11,5	17,5	24	30	36,5
1 Commons	1,0	0,40[2]	24[5]	24	24	30[3]	0,34	0,49	0,65	0,80	0,96
2 and facing	1,2	0,45	24	24	30	24[3]	0,30	0,44	0,58	0,71	0,86
3 bricks with vertical holes	1,4	0,52	24	30	36,5	24[3]	0,27	0,38	0,51	0,62	0,75
4 Solid bricks, facing bricks engineering bricks with vertical holes	1,8	0,68	30	36,5	—	24	0,22	0,31	0,40	0,49	0,59
	1,9[1]										

1 Unit weight. 2 Leaflet, *Proper heat insulation* (Ministry of Housing, West Germany). 3 17.5 cm sufficient for heat insulation, not for acoustical insulation. 4 Can only be built with special sizes. 5 17.5 cm sufficient, if external wall not load bearing, for example skeleton building or cross wall construction.

In most cases the facing is built later. It then is connected with the backing wall with stainless wire anchors. These have to be fixed in the horizontal joints of the backing wall and have a certain inclination to the outside. Ties are also available which are inverted V-shape and so give a good connexion between the two skins. The ties are inserted in the holes of the bricks and these are then filled with mortar. Using solid bricks or engineering bricks without holes is more complicated because holes have to be drilled into the bricks and this process may crack them. The ties can function as damp bridges if they are not used properly.

For this kind of wall only the inner skin is statically calculated, as there is no proper bond between the skins. For load-bearing external walls the thickness should be at least 24 cm.

No voids must be left between facing and backing wall. Also, the vertical joints have to be filled up with mortar. Where heavy rainfall and wind have to be considered, an impervious layer between the two skins should be provided. In this case the backing wall is roughly covered with a mortar of group II, and the facing immediately pressed into this. A waterproofing material can be added to the mortar. If a coat of bituminous paint is given to the backing wall, one should consider whether it can be used to store damp from the inside as well. The bituminous coating operates as damp proof membrane. Damp cannot diffuse to the inside any more. Drying out of the backing wall is no longer possible; this could only be achieved by ventilation. The brick sizes of both skins should be interrelated, and not too many small bricks (DF and NF) should be used.

Cavity brickwork (heat insulation)

There have been many discussions about the quality and use of the cavity wall. But nobody questions that it provides very good weather resistance, especially for areas with heavy rainfall and strong winds.

The air gap retains water which has penetrated the outer skin and keeps it away from the backing wall and, if ventilated, even takes away condensation which may arise from temperature differences. The backing wall stays dry if it is built in the right way. Thermal insulation and living climate of the building stay constant.

The walls are built in different thicknesses. The facing skin is normally 11·5 cm thick. The air gap should be no more than 7 cm. The thickness of the backing wall depends on the requirements of construction and insulation. In one-storey buildings both skins can be 11·5 cm, but the backing wall should be 17·5 cm to achieve better heat insulation.

The outer skin can be built of engineering or facing bricks which are available as DF/NF and 1½ NF. The backing wall can be built of any size of brick. A preference should be given to bricks with holes as they give better heat insulation.

To hold the skins together, 5 stainless ties should be provided per square metre. They should have an inclination towards the outside. In the gap these ties should take the form of a U or V, which allows the water to drop through. Mortar from the faces of each wall within the cavity should be removed to avoid mortar bridges between the skins.

At lintels and reveals the brickwork of both skins has to be separated by moisture barriers. Openings and reveals should have a vertical isolation, which has to be maintained during construction, thus avoiding connexion of inner and outer skins. In cellar walls the brickwork has to be erected solidly up to 30 cm above ground. The air void has to start 20 cm under floor level of the ground floor and go through to the roof without break.

To prevent too rapid air flow, ventilation openings (including windows and doors) should not be made too large. For a 20 m² wall surface, 150 cm² are suggested. The speed of air flow being too high, the heat insulation of the wall deteriorates. (According to studies of Dr Ing. Cammerer an air speed of 4 cm/second is sufficient.)

Ventilation can be achieved by open vertical joints, the installation of metal screens, or special ventilation bricks. The openings should prevent small animals from getting in. At the bottom of the cavity openings are necessary to let out water, which comes down the inside of the facing.

A closed cavity can be incorporated in calculations for heat insulation. If the void is ventilated, only the backing wall must be calculated. To get rid of damp, continuous ventilation is essential. Under certain conditions the heat loss by ventilation can be neglected, as the ventilation at the same time reduces humidity in the inner wall. This improves the heat insulation of the wall. The heat loss by ventilation can thus be balanced with the heat insulation of the backing wall.

The table shows the heat insulation of cavity walls:

Thermal insulation of two-layered walls

Z.	External skin: Kind of brick and unit weight kg/dm³	Thickness of external skin cm	Internal skin Thickness of internal skin cm	cm	Two skin masonry Thermal retention value Brick unit weight of internal skin in kg/dm² 1,0 (WDG)	1,2 (WDG)	1,4 (WDG)
Cavity wall construction							
1	HLz 1,2	11,5	11,5	30	0,80 (I-III)	0,77 (I-III)	0,73 (I-III)
2	VHLz 1,2		17,5	36,5	0,94 (I-III)	0,89 (I-III)	0,84 (I-III)
3	HLz 1,4	11,5	11,5	30	0,77 (I-III)	0,73 (I-III)	0,70 (I-III)
4	VHLz 1,4		17,5	36,5	0,91 (I-III)	0,86 (I-III)	0,80 (I-III)
5	Mz VMz	11,5	11,5	30	0,71 (I-III)	0,68 (I-III)	0,65 (I-III)
6	KHLz		17,5	36,5	0,85 (I-III)	0,81 (I-III)	0,75 (I-III)
7		11,5	11,5	30	0,67 (I-III)	0,64 (I-II)	0,61 (I-II)
8	KMz		17,5	36,5	0,81 (I-III)	0,77 (I-III)	0,71 (I-III)
Two-skin brickwork without cavity							
9	HLz 1,2	11,5	11,5	24	0,59 (I-II)	0,56 (I-II)	0,52 (I)
10	VHLz 1,2		17,5	30	0,74 (I-III)	0,68 (I-III)	0,64 (I-II)
11			24	36,5	0,90 (I-III)	0,84 (I-III)	0,76 (I-III)
12	HLz 1,4	11,5	11,5	24	0,56 (I-II)	0,52 (I)	0,49 (I)
13	VHLz 1,4		17,5	30	0,71 (I-III)	0,66 (I-III)	0,60 (I-II)
14			24	36,5	0,87 (I-III)	0,80 (I-III)	0,73 (I-III)
15	Mz	11,5	11,5	24	0,50 (I)	0,47 (I)	0,44
16	VMz		17,5	30	0,65 (I-III)	0,61 (I-II)	0,55 (I-II)
17	KHLz		24	36,5	0,82 (I-III)	0,75 (I-III)	0,68 (I-III)
18		11,5	11,5	24	0,46 (I)	0,43	0,40
19	KMz		17,5	30	0,61 (I-II)	0,57 (I-II)	0,51 (I)
20			24	36,5	0,78 (I-III)	0,71 (I-III)	0,64 (I-II)

$\frac{1}{\kappa}$ inclusive of 2 cm render and 1.5 cm plaster. With masonry without render the retention value $\frac{1}{\kappa}$ reduces by 0.027 m²h⁰/kcal.

Prefabricated wall slabs in brick

More and more one-storey high wall slabs of brick or ceramic tiles are used. In Germany and other countries bricks with holes have been developed which are very suitable for the fabrication of one-storey high wall slabs. These slabs consist of large size hollow bricks of a size 25 cm². The slabs can be produced in different thicknesses, preferably 16·5 cm and 19 cm.

Being combined slabs they can also be load-bearing. The weight of one slab is determined by the unit weight of the bricks, their thickness and the type of slab.

Slabs for external walls have either render on both sides, or applied facing bricks, engineering bricks or ceramic tiles. Some factories supply the slabs complete with fixed windows, doors or frames.

By using bricks the weight of the slabs is kept low; the required

heat insulation can also be provided. The good physical properties of brick continue; adjustment between outside air and inside air is possible.

If the facing is of engineering brick or ceramic tile, the backing brick wall has to have sufficient damp storage capacity. The same conditions are valid as in normal cladding with engineering brick or ceramic material. Also the ceramic industry supplies prefabricated slabs, about 1 m². Their thickness is dependent on the type of ceramic tile used. One producer uses a synthetic mortar for the joints; this makes the slab relatively flexible. The slabs are fixed in front of the backing wall, leaving a ventilated void behind.

Mortar and efflorescence

All joints of cladding and backing wall in facing brickwork should be completely filled with mortar of group II. The mortar should be pliant and easy to handle. It should have good cohesion and after hardening still be elastic and lasting. It should resist moisture from outside but still allow internal condensation to find its way out. So-called P. M. binders (render and mortar binders) have been developed which are made of portland cement clinker limestone and air-entrained formations. High hydraulic tufa lime is also appropriate as binder for facing walls.

The sand should be of mixed grain and free of destructive elements. Not more than 3 per cent of the weight should be chemically affected. The choice of the right sand is important for a good mortar as a fine grain needs much binder; otherwise the mortar can become too "rich". A higher proportion of binder encourages cracking in the mortar and a tendency to shrink. The mortar then lets water through. Such a condition cannot be accepted in outside walls which must be impervious. The following compositions are good for mortar:

Grain	0 –0·2 mm	Proportion	10–20%
	0·2–1 mm		30–40%
	1 –3 mm		40–60%

Reagents are often added which make the mortar water-repellent. The manufacturer's instructions have to be strictly followed. These reagents should not affect the damp transmission of the mortar. If it is very warm during use, this kind of mortar can dry out too quickly and cannot absorb water any more because of being water-repellent. Then the mortar may come away from the brickwork. Also, admixtures of anti-freeze additives have to be kept small, to prevent later efflorescence, as some of them include calcium chloride.

It also has to be pointed out that mortar with a dry to stiff consistency on one hand avoids sullying bricks during the building process, whilst on the other hand having a high volume of pores and capillaries.

By admixing synthetic resin dispersions the elasticity of cement mortar and its cohesion can be improved. Cement mortar with synthetic resin dispersions generally has a high impermeability and it allows diffusion of damp. But the different dispersions (PVA, Butadienestyrol and others) have different properties. One should investigate which one is the most suitable. No liquefier should be added to cement mortar as this would make it stiff and adhesion to the bricks would be bad.

In brickwork which is exposed to bad weathering conditions, pointing the joints, and the right consistency of the mortar, are important. The pointing should be flush with the surface of the bricks. Fresh mortar should be scraped out from all joints to a depth of 1·5 mm before every pause in work. Then all loose bits of mortar have to be brushed off and wall dampened. For cleaning the brickwork only pure water and a steel brush should be used. Only in certain cases may 1 per cent acetic acid be added. It is not advisable to use hydrochloric acid as it is too aggressive and under certain circumstances calcium chloride can separate out. This makes adhesion of the mortar more difficult, and the salt may lead to efflorescence. After cleaning with acid the wall has to be hosed down with a sufficient amount of water. Pointing should only be done in suitable weather, not in heavy rain or bright sunshine. The mortar for joints has to be used within two hours after it is made, otherwise it will start to harden. It should be mixed by machine. It is best to point after the brickwork has settled, as its mortar has then hardened. If it is dry the wall has to be made wet first, otherwise the brick at once absorbs the water from the mortar. The pointing should not only be made flush, but should be pressed firmly into the joint. Only then does it achieve a good connexion to the walling mortar. The joints must be dense and without holes; they should be flush with the brick. Joints over filled so that projections occur are unsatisfactory as water and dirt can rest on them.

The process of pointing is in two steps:

1. Vertical joints first, horizontal joints afterwards.
2. The above process reversed.

In the first step connexion between wall mortar and pointing mortar should be achieved, in the second the surface is made even by trowelling. In dry weather the wall has to be made wet a second time after the pointing.

Special care has to be taken at scaffolding holes, as they tend to be loose, permeable points in external walls. Instead of scaffolding holes, holding bolts can be rammed into the joints, which then hold the timbers of the scaffolding. These holding bolts have a width of 8 to 10 cm. As no bricks need be left out, the pointing of the joint presents no difficulty. The danger of moisture penetration from scaffolding holes is much reduced by this method. Lightning rods, aerials and pipe clamps have to be at a certain inclination, to keep water off the wall.

Also important is the composition of the mortar for joints. This mortar has to be frost- and weather-resistant, but also has to allow damp diffusion after hardening. Too rich a mortar is in danger of producing shrinkage cracks, through which weather can penetrate. To obtain good pointing mortar the following mix is recommended:

1 volume unit portland cement, 1 volume unit tufa, 3 to 4 volume units of sand of sharp-edged, mixed grain of 0 to maximum 2 mm grain. The proportion of ingredients depends on the grain of sand.

Adding tufa makes even relatively sandy mortar water-resistant. Tufa also can combine chemically with water soluble hydrate of chalk. If a hydraulic binding agent is made use of, cement and tufa should be used for the pointing mortar whilst with an air hardening lime mortar as a masonry mortar, tufa plus hydrated lime should be incorporated. It is advisable for outside walls to use a masonry mortar containing tufa. The use of a water-repellent additive (Ceresit, Lugato) does for example not obviate the need for the right choice of grain. Coloured admixtures often produce joints which contrast with

the masonry. The amount added should not be too large, as coloured admixtures reduce the denseness and solidity of the mortar: they should not exceed 5 per cent of the weight of the binding agent and should not be affected by it. Some of the colours are:

Colour tone Material

White	Titanium dioxide, titanium white
Yellow	Ferric oxide yellow
Red	Ferric oxide red, Spanish ferric oxide
Blue	Cobalt blue, Cölin blue
Green	Chrome oxide green, chrome oxyhydrate green, permanent green
Brown	Ferric oxide brown
Black	Ferric oxide black, manganese black

Efflorescence is caused by soluble salts, contained in minerals, which are dissolved out of the centre of the wall and are transported to the surface by moving moisture. As the moisture evaporates on the surface the salts remain. The greater part of efflorescence is caused by inorganic mineral salts (sulphates, carbonates, and chlorides), more seldom by salts containing metals.

The tendency to effloresce is the greater the more the wall is soaked with moisture and the slower the evaporation. In most cases the efflorescence becomes apparent in spring: as the heavy and sometimes long-lasting penetration of moisture into the wall in autumn and winter favours a solution of these salts, their sediments then form on the surface. A permanent penetration of moisture, caused by subsoil water or rising damp from the ground, can lead to efflorescence over a long period. The salts can be contained in the bricks, in the water, in the binder or in the sand. Therefore it is important to avoid efflorescence by choosing the right materials. In unfavourable cases quantities of salt of only 1/1000 of the weight of the mortar can cause efflorescence. This shows how difficult it is to take preventive measures.

A first source of moisture is constructional moisture (that contained in the materials) which under certain circumstances can be increased by use of wet stone or brick or influences from outside. As mentioned before, efflorescence can also be caused by constant moisture, namely by insufficient isolation of elements, and damp from the ground. In this process it is also possible that efflorescent substances penetrate into the walls from the ground. Another source can be water from condensation, when damp cannot be removed sufficiently. One has to distinguish permanently soluble salts (sulphates, chlorides) from temporarily soluble salts (calcium carbonate). The first kind effloresce very fast; normally they are soon washed away by rain and wind. If calcium sulphate is the cause, then efflorescence disappears very slowly.

A direct relationship exists between use of anti-frost components, or washing the walls with acid, and efflorescence. While anti-frost components often contain chlorides, which are soluble, it is possible that although the wall is washed with acid, already dissolved salts can get into the joints and then effloresce again. This can be avoided by cleaning the wall carefully with water. While it is possible to remove occurring efflorescence by dry brushing, efflorescence from permanent moisture is more difficult to remove. Nowadays, chemical

(Continued on page 251)

FAMILY HOUSES

1

2

3

1 (Page 21) One-family house in Nienberge. Brick walls. Framework of window walls, gutter boards and barge boards of tiled roofs, are painted.
⋏ Prof. Harald Deilmann
2 One-family house near Zürich. Facing brickwork to the garden side: rendering on the street side as well as on lintels; blind boxes and panels between windows are painted a contrasting colour. Barge boards and gutter boards are glossed white.
3 One-family house in Münster/Westphalia. Load-bearing walls and panels faced with brick; rendered surfaces are painted. Window frames and balcony doors are glossed. Slate roof.
⋏ Prof. Harald Deilmann
4 One-family house in Küssnacht/Switzerland. Structure emphasized through contrasting materials. Boarding beneath gable impregnated. Roof soffite, gable boards, gutter boards, windows and doors are glossed white.
⋏ Schärli Brothers
5 Country house in Denmark. Timber construction with shingles. Window frames and doors painted white, push-up blinds glossed blue.
⋏ Erik Möller
6 Holiday house in Piandi Sole/Italy. A property situated on a steep slope. External staircase construction and lower floor in rough stone; ground-floor walls partly in brick, rendered and whitewashed, partly in structural timber boarded with untreated larch.
⋏ Sergio Pizzera

4

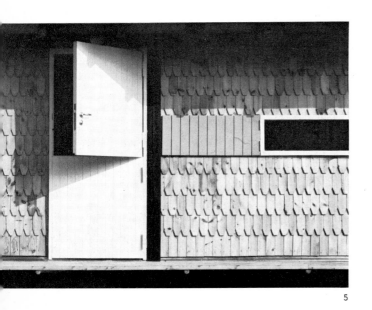

5

6

7 One-family house in Cologne. Steel skeleton; façade panels in rendered, painted brickwork. Panels of the longitudinal façades clad with cross-boarding of Afzelia. Stanchions and gutter boards glossed. Windows dark grey, louvered panels glossed white. ⅄ Joachim Schürmann

8 One-family house in Darmstadt. Reinforced concrete skeleton with prefabricated brick panels formed into vertical strips. Garage door red pine. Steel columns of the porch are glossed. Double entrance doors are covered with melamine-faced plastic. ⅄ Hans-Günter Hofmann

9 Section from a group of one-family houses near Copenhagen. Whitewashed brickwork. Fascia cladding and the soffite of the protecting roofs in pine. Columns and windows in teak. ⅄ Jørgen Bo and Vilhelm Wohlert

7

8

9

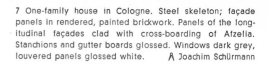

10

10 One-family house near Athens. Reinforced concrete skeleton with both its boarded face, and rendered brick panels, painted with a mineral paint. Rough stone on the ground floor. Windows, shutters, external doors, and balcony parapets are painted in a contrasting colour. Metal rods of the loggia façade are glossed black.   Ⱥ Aris Konstantinidis

11 One-family house in Uitikon/Switzerland. Reinforced concrete skeleton with facing brick. Front side of the continuous concrete beams painted white. By contrast the window-frames and spandrels beneath the windows are dark.   Ⱥ U. Abegg

11

12 Country house near Zürich. Ground-floor walls with specially made extra large bricks. Brickwork in the upper floor rendered smooth and painted with a white rubber-base paint. Lintels in exposed concrete, window spandrels and terrace parapets clad in grey glass mosaic. Windows constructed in timber and aluminium.   ∤ Paul Keller

13 House in Rotterdam. Black/purple hard-burnt exposed brick. Red brown Afrormosia planking with a clear varnish. Exposed concrete areas painted with light grey-coloured cement paint. Windows glossed white.   ∤ Van den Broek and Bakema

12

13

14 House in Bielefeld. Emphasized separation of the two floors through materials and colour. Smooth, recessed, rendered areas on the upper floor painted with a special paint (Hermidur). Exposed concrete framing to the upper floor and side walls painted white. Timber on the ground-floor wall has a colourless varnish. Aluminium windows.   ∤ Gregor Wannenmacher

14

15

15 House in Herrsching on the Ammersee. Structure of six steel frames. Street side of the living area panelled with gas concrete slabs to one-storey height and planked with vertical, impregnated fir strips. Sheet cladding of the upper and lower fascias is gloss painted to contrast with the fir. Walls of the ancillary rooms in brick, whitewashed. Window frames painted with white gloss paint.　　　　　　　 Å Kurt Ackermann

16

17

16 Holiday house in Aeschlen/Switzerland. Lower floor in exposed concrete, upper floor in timber construction with horizontal planking in natural fir. Roofing of asbestos cement slates (Eternit). Cladding of the barge boards, of the gutter boards and of the balcony parapets in enamelled asbestos cement slabs (Pelichrom).　　　Å Werner Küenzi

17 One-family house in Forch/Switzerland. Solid wall construction in brickwork. Rendering painted with rubber-base paint. Window and gutter boards glossed white. Roof covered with asbestos slates (Eternit).　　　　　　　Å Jacques de Stoutz

18 Block of owner-occupier flats in Zürich. Balcony and terrace parapet over the garage in exposed concrete painted with a mineral paint, similarly the end walls. Asbestos cement coverings to barge boards, gutter boards, the front face of the continuous concrete floor beams, and the whole area of the plinth, are painted in a contrasting grey rubber-base paint. Windows and roller blinds of Normandy pine, lacquered brown.

ᴧ Rolf Kamer

19 House in Zumikon/Switzerland. Walls clad partly in yellow facing brick and partly in dark grey asbestos cement panels (Eternit). Windows and window posts coated in colourless varnish.

ᴧ Andreas Eichhorn

18

19

20

20 House in Munich. End walls in rendered brick, on the garden side recessed external wall, horizontally planked, with continuous loggia. Rendered and planked areas painted with a rubber-base paint (Diwagolan). Window-wall units with lifting or sliding doors are glossed.
    ⋀ Helga and Adolf Schnierle

21 House in Gaggenau. Construction with standardized precast concrete frames. External wall slabs clad partly with vertical timber strips, partly with asbestos cement slabs (Eternit). Roof in corrugated Eternit sheets.   ⋀ E. Dreiner and E. Runge

21

22 Holiday house in Lenzerheide/Switzerland. Ground floor and external fireplace in solid wall construction of concrete and brick, rendered smooth and painted white with rubber-base paint. Bedroom floor in timber-frame construction with horizontal timber planking and paint-impregnated. Underside of roof, coverings to barge boards and gutter boards as well as all windows and shutters painted with a white gloss.   ⋀ H. J. Ochsner

22

23

24

23 House with post office and doctor's practice in Graubünden. *In situ* concrete construction with exposed boarded finish. Horizontally planked timber (left of illustration) impregnated with a reddish colour. Wall cladding of the roof flanks in copper. Staircase and peripheral walls of rough stone.   ⅄ Dr Justus Dahinden
24 House in Mandello Lario/Italy. Load-bearing skeleton in reinforced concrete, ground-floor walls partly in natural stone. Projecting compound walls on the upper floor and wall panels on the ground floor clad with pitch pine painted with matt lacquer. Gutter board painted with rubber-base paint.   ⅄ Gian Angelini
25 House with indoor swimming pool in Palm Springs/California. Walls of the swimming pool (solid to protect from sunshine) from intrinsically coloured concrete elements. On the section in the background a wall with concrete fretwork. Screening (on the left of the illustration) in steel frame, partly filled with light concrete slabs, partly with drawn metal members.   ⅄ Stewart Williams
26 Country house in Wissembourg/France. Steel construction. Wall panels of rendered brick, painted with rubber-base paint. All steel parts sandblasted, red-leaded and painted with lacquer (Ducolux). Terrace laid out entirely with hard-burnt tiles. Foundation walls in rough stone.   ⅄ Walter Brune

25

26

27 Forest house in Düsseldorf. Whitewashed brickwork. Gutter
boards clad with shingles. Timber of the balcony balustrade
coated with colourless impregnant.
Ⓐ City building authority of Düsseldorf
28 Atrium one-family houses in Reinach/Switzerland. Load-bearing
walls in exposed brickwork. Gutter-board coverings and lintels
in asbestos cement. Ⓐ Ulrich Löw and Theodor Manz

27

28

29

30

29 House on Lake Maggiore. Upper floor rests on load-bearing walls of natural stone. Main living floor itself is in concrete construction with compound external walls which are planked vertically with fir boarding.
Ʌ Rodolfo Carabelli

30 One-family house in Odenwald. Bearing masonry on the ground floor from worked natural stone slabs. Exposed concrete and rendered areas of the upper floor painted with rubber-base paint (Amphibolin). Garage doors and windows treated with gloss paint. Larch cladding of the side façade and of the balcony balustrade is lacquered.

31 One-family house in Bochum. Constructed in stonework with black rendering (Steinwerke Kupferdreh). Roof gutter boards clad with small tiles (5 x 5 cm). Forming a covered walkway, the continuous concrete projection is painted white. Windows glossed. Window spandrels on the ground floor of asbestos cement with coloured surface (Glasal).
Ʌ Roman J. Reiser

31

32 Group of one-family houses in Rome. Reinforced concrete skeleton. Additional V-shaped concrete supports for the cantilevered circulation and balcony areas which in places project out 5 m. The supports are veneered with granulated, dark blue marble. Emphasis of the strong division of the complex through numerous surface structures and colours. Walls under the main terraces covered with dark brown facing tiles (hard burnt) 5 x 20 cm. Fascia walls faced with hard burnt tiles. Timber cladding surfaces of 5-cm. Douglas Fir vertical strips. Balcony balustrades and deep gutter boards, which project out considerably, are clad with ceramic relief tiles (5 x 10 x 0.4 cm.). Roof surfaces covered with zinc yellow glass mosaic because they can be seen from nearby high blocks. Dark blue, glazed floor tiles (20 x 10 cm.) on the terraces. Peripheral walls of worked natural stone. Ŗ Dr Lorenzo Monardo

33 Estate in Manosque/France. Powerful delineation of the structure through colour contrasts. Solid wall construction, rendered smooth and painted with rubber-base paint. Window bars and loggia balustrade of square steel sections, partly with armoured glass panes.
Å G. Candilis, A. Josic and S. Woods
34 Holiday houses in Leysin/Switzerland. Bearing walls of light constructional bricks. Rendered with incised rough squares, whitewashed. Barge boards and recessed entrance walls boarded with deal. On the front façades (not visible in the illustration) cladding of enamelled asbestos cement sheets. Roof: brightly pigmented synthetic covering on foil on timber joists (internal drainage).
Å M. Weber and I. Petrowitsch, Rud. A. Schoch and R. Möller
35 Holiday village 'Bosco della Bella' near Fornasetti/Switzerland. All the houses are prefabricated on the same system. Laminated timber construction, resting on concrete foundations. Cladding with 40 x 40 cm. asbestos cement tiles (Eternit) apart from the glass front façades. Coverings of the barge boards on the front façades with galvanised iron sheet. Frames of the recessed window walls in fir, fixed panels with opaque, coloured glass.
Å Dr Justus Dahinden

33

36

37

36 Holiday house in Amden/Switzerland. Solid wall construction with overlapping planking, impregnated with colour. Roof and gable areas covered with 40 x 30 cm. asbestos cement slates (Eternit), double layered. Gutter board covering in copper. Window and window shutters painted with gloss paint. Ѧ Anton Monn

37 Terrace houses in Klampenborg/Denmark. Walls in facing brick. Balcony parapets between the house volumes of white enamelled steel sheet. Gutter and barge boards painted with white oil paint. Ѧ Prof. Arne Jacobsen

38 One-family houses in the ENI holiday village 'Corte di Cadore' near Cortina d'Ampezzo. Rough, boarded, concrete crosswalls (walls acting as beams). Front walls support the separated and higher, snow roof. On the front façades compound slabs with coloured synthetic surfaces. Balconies on reinforced concrete cantilever beams. Black stove-enamelled steel sections. Timber naturally impregnated. Ѧ Eduardo Gellner

38

39

40

39 Group of atrium houses in Gäddvik/Finland. Structural timber with painted asbestos cement slabs (Eternit). Atrium walls (not visible on the illustration) of whitewashed brick work. The timber façade of the garage doors on the groundfloor of the street side is colour impregnated. ∧ Jaakko Laapotti

40 Houses in Stetten/Valley of the Rems. Lower floor, supporting walls and chimneys in exposed concrete. Upper-floor walls, whitewashed facing limestone. Guttering boards in redwood. ∧ Kammerer & Belz

41 Terrace houses in Bochum. Lower-floor façade walls, gutter facings and garages all rendered. Sides of upper floors facing the street clad with ceramic mosaic 5 x 5 cm. (see detail illustration). Garage and entrance doors, white gloss paint. ∧ Roman J. Reiser

41

42

42 Group of one-family houses in Münster‚
phalia. Walls in facing brick. Slate roof. ‚
facings rendered to form a strong contra‚
means of colour. Window and door frames ‚
painted. Door panels of front doors cc‚
with melamine-faced plastic.
                           Å Prof. Harald De‚

43 Terrace houses in Hamburg. Brick wal‚
the ground-floor and return walls ren‚
smooth and painted with rubber-base pai‚
wagolan) in alternating colours. Upper ‚
with overlapping planking impregnated ‚
Xylamon with addition of Kasseler Braun‚
dows as well as gutter and barge b‚
brigthly contrasted.   Å Atmer & M‚

43

44

44 Terrace houses near Copenhagen. Red facing brick. Gutters, fallpipes, barge boards and windows painted with white gloss; retaining walls in dark grey cement paint.
ᴀ Prof. Arne Jacobsen

45 One-family terrace houses in Hamburg. Brick side walls and gutter boards rendered and painted in two colours with rubber-base paint. Chimneys and entrance sides in facing brick. On the garden sides (as shown in the illustration) and on the walls of the upperfloors on the street side, vertical timber boarding, colour impregnated. Windows painted gloss white. The standard sunblinds provide a powerful contrast.
ᴀ Schramm & Elingius

45

46

47

48

46 Residential area of Oberlinde
Rendered solid wall construction. Struc
ure emphasized through strong exchang
of colour in the rubber-base paint (He
bol). The overall multi-coloured effe
is achieved by the coloured walls beir
alternately at right angles to, or parall
to, the building line.
          ⋔ Nassau Homestea
47 Terrace houses near Amsterdam. Er
walls and panels on front façade
facing brick. Timber framework of th
window wall painted gloss white. Infi
panels on the upper floors of coloure
glass (Detopak). Entrance doors covere
with red melamine faced plastic. Ro
gutter boards clad with white glos
painted square-section sheet metal.
48 Terrace houses in Hengelo/Hollan
Walls of yellowish grey facing bric
By contrast the exposed floor slabs a
painted with light grey rubber-bas
paint. Front doors, window posts ar
gutter boards blue gloss-painted. Windo
frames dark grey, casement frame
white. Vertical timber boarding near th
entrances is light grey.
          ⋔ Van den Broek and Baken

50

51

52

53

49 (Page 41) Terrace houses in Düsseldorf. Wall panels in quartzite with Roman cramps. Aluminium window frames and garage doors.   ⋀ Klaus Wülfing
50 House in Düsseldorf. The front faces of the exposed floor slabs and the bands at the base of windows all clad with marble (white Christallino). Balcony balustrades of enamelled aluminium alternate in colour from floor to floor.
                                                                                                                                                                                            ⋀ Josef Hellenkamp

51 Corner house in Cologne. Reinforced concrete skeleton with brick panels. Front faces of the exposed floor slabs form a bright contrast. Balcony parapets of exposed concrete. All external walls and parapets painted with a rubber-base paint (Indurin).   ⋀ Hans Schilling
52 Combined house and shop in Düsseldorf. Walls clad with hard burnt brick. Window spandrels of vertical timber strips. Front faces of the exposed floor slabs painted with white rubber-base paint.   ⋀ Josef Hellenkamp
53 Block of flats in Tessin/Switzerland. The cantilevered floors form terraces; balustrades of blue-grey armourplate glass fixed to square-section posts taken from ground floor to the edge of the roof. Walls partly rendered and painted with rubber-base paint, partly clad with timber boarding, colour impregnated. Undersides of the cantilever slabs, façades and the exposed concrete ground floor walls similarly painted with rubber-base paint.   ⋀ Alex Huber

54

55

56

57

58

54—57 Buildings in various residential quarters of Munich. Their overall effect was produced through emphasizing in colour the structure of the building. Throughout, powerful colours were used and contrasts were formed through the delineation of the floors, parapets and balconies. All the walls were rendered.
54 Painted with rubber-base paint. Karl Wienzierl (brown block) Gordon Ludwig and Franz Raab (grey block).
55 Painted with Vulkanit rubber-base paint.
Ⓐ The Federal Railway authorities in Munich
56 Window infill panels form a bright contrast. The panels on the stair well are decorated linearly. The paint is Diwagolan rubber base paint. Ⓐ Harald Loebermann
57 The paint is Vulkanit rubber-base paint. Ⓐ Friedr. F. Haindl
58 Apartment blocks in Hamburg. Prefabricated external wall elements. The cladding is medium-size ceramic mosaic in two colours.
Ⓐ Atmer & Marlow

59 Block of flats in Bremen. Rendered walls painted with rubber-base paint (Amphibolin). When the façades are painted with a dark colour the balconies are a light colour and *vice versa*.
Ⓐ Dr Säume, G. Hafemann, Dr Reichow, Prof. May
60 Terrace houses in Munich. Rendered walls painted with Basis Propiofan rubber-base paint. Ground floor clad with compound slabs. Ⓐ Prof. Franz Ruf
61 Terrace houses in Berlin. Walls rendered with a fine pebble dash. The front faces of the exposed floor slabs and the gutter fascia are contrastingly white. Balconies are steel-framed with parapets of asbestos cement slabs. Ⓐ Gerhard Krebs

59

60

61

62 Block of flats with a church in an estate in Acilia/Italy. Reinforced concrete skeleton construction with brick panels. The rendered lintels and the slatted roller shutters are painted the same colour. In the case of the church, the exposed skeleton, lintels and gutter boards were painted a dark colour to contrast.　Ѧ Giuseppe Perugini
63 Combined flats and shops in Latina/Italy. Reinforced concrete skeleton (looking up at the balcony soffites gives a relief effect). Brick panels and prefabricated window units. All visible concrete, including staircase, porch and lintels, painted the same colour. Rendered balcony soffits painted. Window infill panels and balcony balustrades of enamelled steel sheets.　Ѧ Riccardo Cerocchi

62

63

64

65

64 Maisonettes on a London estate. Walls of timber frames with asbestos cement façade slabs (Eternit). Windows and doors gloss-painted. Balcony parapets of painted steel frames with armourplate glass. Soffits of the bedroom floors painted white.　Ѧ Hubert Bennett
65 Apartment house in Munich. Walls rendered in Russian green. Floor division and balcony claddings white; on the whole the party walls at the back of the balcony are also in contrasting white.　Ѧ Planning Office Mund
66 Apartment house in Helsinki. Reinforced concrete skeleton. End façades in facing brick. Window spandrels and gutter-board claddings of coloured glass (Detopak). Balcony balustrades of square steel-section with hardened glass and timber handrail. Rendered surfaces painted with rubber-base paint.　Ѧ Lauri Silvennoinen

66

67 Section of a block of flats in Amsterdam. Bands of facing brick. Window area frames gloss-painted; areas of coloured opaque glass are inserted in places (Detopak). Soffites and walls of the balconies painted with rubber-base paint.   A. Staat
68 Block of flats near Amsterdam. Reinforced concrete skeleton with brick panels on the ground floor. Front faces of the exposed floor slabs corrugated. Window infills of coloured glass (Detopak).

67

68

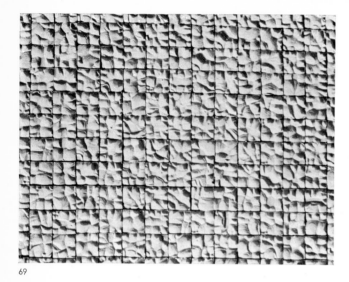

69

70

71

72

69 House in Milan. Reinforced concrete skeleton with hollow blocks. All the external walls are clad with green ceramic mosaic (2 x 2 cm.) with a hammered surface (see detail of illustration). Metal window-frames and mullions anodised black. Blinds of Swedish fir. ↑ Gian Carlo Malchiodi
70 Block of flats in Bergamo. Reinforced concrete skeleton, lintels and parapets painted with mineral paint. Panel walls clad in 25 x 6 cm. faience. Window infill panels of enamelled sheet steel. Windows and slatted roller shutters gloss-painted. ↑ Carlo Panigada
71 Block of flats in Frankfurt/Main. Reinforced concrete skeleton. Stair-well cladding of naturally anodised square corrugated sheets (Aluform). Infills of the same material but coated with a synthetic (Aluform 200). ↑ Prof. Alfred Caspari
72 Section of a block of flats in Basle. Facing brickwork. ↑ Rickenbacher & Baumann

73

73 Blocks of flats in Biel/Switzerland. 30-cm. bricks, rough cast. Fine rubbing-over in cement mortar. Parapets and gutter boards in concrete. Rubber-base paint; parapets and gutter boards in strong contrasting colour, balcony partition walls in lighter tone of same colour. Slatted roller shutters gloss-painted.   A René Devaux

74 Block of flats in Thonen/France. The whole building is rendered and painted with a rubber-base paint. Front faces of the exposed floor slabs project slightly. Recessed parapets, being strongly coloured, stand out clearly and divide up the façade.

75 House in Hanover. Crosswalls of yellow Dutch hard burnt facing bricks. Infill panels clad with white medium-sized mosaic 5 x 5 cm. Oregon pine coated with natural coloured varnish.   A Richter & Wilke

76 Block of flats for renting in Milan. Exposed parts of the reinforced concrete frame and the rendered cladding over the shops painted with rubber-base paint. All the external walls of the upper floor clad with small ceramic mosaic. Recessed intermediary floor clad with timber. Blind box covers and window spandrels of the projecting central part of enamelled steel sheet. Cast glass balcony balustrades.

77 Block of flats with offices and stores in Pirmasens. Structural walls clad with asbestos cement façade sheets (Fulgurit) and painted with rubber-base paint.   A R. Heil

78 Block of flats in Bad Wörishofen. Rendered walls painted with rubber-base paint. Balcony façades and window surrounds white. The sides of the balcony parapets are in the darker colour of the window frames.   A J. Schneider

74

75

76

77

78

79

80

79 Slab blocks of flats in Wiesbaden. Side façades rendered and painted. Parapets clad with hard burnt bricks in panels in two
colours.   ⋏ Friedrich Wilhelm Bossert and Ulla Haldy
80 Block of flats in Ludwigshafen. Front faces of the exposed floor slabs, window reveals and roof gutter boards in exposed concrete
painted grey. Walls clad with hard burnt bricks in panels (Gail). Balcony balustrade of natural grey asbestos cement strips.
                                                                    ⋏ Wilhelm Schmidt

81 Block of flats in Bellach/Switzerland. Reinforced concrete frame construction. Panels in brick. Balcony parapets and window infill panels of prefabricated concrete elements. Rubber-base paint in four colours. The sun blinds are uniform throughout to create a contrast. Å Heinz Walthard

82 Block of flats and shops in Biel/Switzerland. Reinforced concrete structure. Panels and façades rendered. Render and exposed concrete areas painted (Muresko). Å Rob. A. Meystre

83 Block of flats in Lucerne. Brick cladding. Exposed concrete parts painted with rubber-base paint. Balcony parapets have inset panels of hardened glass. Å Schärli Brothers

81

82

83

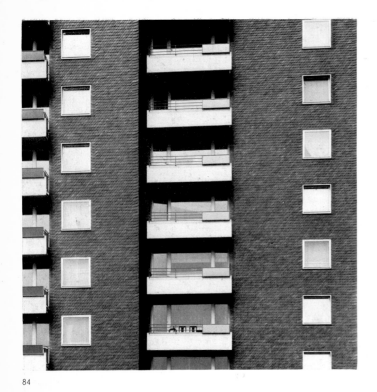

84

85

86

84 Point blocks in Remscheid. Structural walls. Hanging slates from the Moselle form the cladding. Concrete balcony parapets rendered and painted white with mineral paint. ⋏ Walter Arns

85 Block of flats in Schwelm. Structural walls. Cladding of intrinsically coloured asbestos cement sheets (Eternit Colorit), partly vertical, partly horizontal. Balcony parapets of concrete, painted the colour of the cross bands.
⋏ Schwelmer Building Society

86 Blocks of flats in Wolfsburg. Large prefabricated concrete panels, each one storey high and the width of one room. Surfaced with medium sized ceramic mosaic 5 x 5 cm. Joints, balconies and windows painted a contrasting white. Light walls of stair wells of glass bricks. ⋏ Hans Tiedemann

87

88

87 Block of flats in the suburb of 'Västra Skogen' near Stockholm. Parapet bands of square-section gloss-painted aluminium. Panels between the windows of painted asbestos cement slabs.
⋏ Jarl Bjurström

88 Block of flats in Gelsenkirchen. Cladding of all external walls in enamelled asbestos cement sheets (Eternit-Glasal) contrasted with anodized aluminium ridged sheets. ⋏ Schiffm—

89 Blocks of flats in Milan. All external walls clad with ceramic tiles (10 x 10 cm and 10 x 20 cm.). Window wall units and blinds gloss-painted, undersides of the balconies painted with mineral paint. Å Carlo Perogalli

89

90

90 Block of flats in Milan. Rendered walls. Continuous balcony screens of brick trellis work. Cast glass balcony balustrades. The low part of the building is clad with hard-burnt bricks. The infill panels of enamelled steel sheet.

91 Section from a block of flats with staggered floors, in Lugano. The cube-like projecting balconies of exposed concrete painted with mineral paint give a strong visual effect. The adjacent balustrade of cast glass in a channel frame, timber handrail. External walls rendered as also the undersides of the balcony slabs. Å Luigi Chiesa

91

92 Section from a block of flats in Milan. Reinforced concrete frame construction. Wall cladding of the masonry panels of glazed relief tiles. Window infill panels in wrought iron. Window frames as also the front faces and undersides of the continuous concrete floors painted a light colour.
⋏ Prof. Pio Montesi

92

94

93 Apartment house in Uster/Switzerland. Cladding with brownish-red relief bricks. Lintels and panels on the narrow windows of prefabricated concrete parts. Timber frame of the windows and the Venetian blinds white gloss.

94 Block of flats and offices in Nuremberg. External wall cladding of light metal sheets, brushed matt and naturally anodized (the solid parts are interrupted by glass). Ground floor in colour treated exposed concrete.
⋏ Harald Loebermann

95

96

95 Block of flats in Vårby near Stockholm. Façade walls in facing brick. Parapets clad with asbestos cement corrugated sheets (Eternit) and painted white.　　　Å Dr Andreas Carstens
96 Block of flats in Milan. Masonry walls entirely clad with small ceramic mosaic. The yellow blinds form a contrast. Rendered infill panels on the stair well and the roof gutter boards painted white.
97 Block of flats in Basle. Walls in facing brick. Recessed roof floor rendered and painted. Roof continued out to form a pergola. Balcony parapets of intrinsically coloured concrete.

98 Block of flats near Lugano. Panelled walls in rendered brick. The stair well, the cantilevered floor plate and the ceiling structure of exposed concrete painted a contrasting colour. The whole building is painted with rubber-base paint (bearing parts white; panels green, orange and purple).　　　Å Peppo Brivio
99 Section from a block of flats in Langenaes/Denmark. Reinforced concrete frame. Balcony partition walls of prefabricated concrete, painted in two alternating colours. Balcony parapets of similarly prefabricated concrete elements, painted white with rubber-base paint. Ground-floor plinth of exposed concrete, in a contrasting dark colour.　　　Å Salling-Mortensen

97

98

99

100

100 Residential estate in Munich. Rendered masonry walls. The basic colour is divided up by white lines. Wind-bracing stair towers and concrete balcony parapets in a contrasting darker blue. This colour repeats in the triangular frieze on the parapet of the roof terrace. Woodwork of the roof of the pergola in a harmonizing colour. Lower buildings are dark with light balcony parapets. All the paints are rubber-base type (Herboi).
 Å Otto Roth

101 Group of houses near Aarhus/Denmark. Bearing construction in reinforced concrete, non-bearing parts of concrete prefabricated elements. Rubber-base paint in two colours, and to emphasize visually the horizontal lines. Windows and door walls on the sides of the loggias are in timber. Å Salling-Mortensen

102

103

104

102 Block of flats in a residential quarter of Munich. Wa
rendered and painted with rubber-base paint (Diwa
Balcony balustrades and front faces of the continuous cc
floors contrasted in a light colour. Balustrades partly
crete and partly timber. Å E. N
103 Block of flats in Milan. Walls of red facing brick.
areas and front façades of the continuous floors in e
concrete. Window infill panels painted white, blind bc
blue enamelled steel sheet. Å Attilio
104 Block of flats in Düsseldorf. External wall cladding
nately coloured or white ceramic split tiles (Gail).
Å Jochen Heb
(Note: the term 'split tiles' refers to those which are
in pairs and afterwards divided)

105 Block of flats in Manching near Munich. Rendered str
walls entirely painted with mineral paint (Keim). Fa
balcony parapets and rear walls as well as the front fa
the continuous concrete floors in contrasting white. Th
colour on the roof floor forms the upper termination
front façade. The wall of the side stair well of cc
honeycomb. Å Architectural Department of the B
Welfare Authorities,
106 Section from the estate 'Neue Vahr' in Bremen. Re
walls with symmetrically arranged groups of balconie
tones of rubber-base paint used (Basis Mowilith).
Å Prof.

105

106

107 Block of flats in Berlin. Bearing walls in exposed concrete and painted in two colours with a rubber-base paint (Diwagolan). Balcony balustrades of asbestos cement.

⋏ Hans-Dieter Bolle

108 Block of flats in Geneva. Reinforced concrete frame. Balcony parapets of variously coloured, decorative armoured glass. The sun blinds of uniform colour create a strong impact. ⋏ Addor and Juilliard Honegger Brothers

107

109

110

109 Housing estate 'Tours de Carouge' in Geneva. All the blocks are constructed of exposed concrete with prefabricated elements. External walls in uniform colour, balcony partition walls painted blue and the undersides white with a rubber-base paint. The rows of holes on the parapets serve both to air the balconies and to create an ornamental appearance to the whole building.

Ⓐ Architectural office 'Tours de Carouge'

110 Section from a block of flats in Düsseldorf. Reinforced concrete frame. Balcony parapets of prefabricated, reddish, exposed aggregate slabs. Windows painted. Ⓐ Prof. Nothelfer

111—113

111—113 Maisonette blocks in London. All the buildings are of reinforced concrete frame construction and under the direction of Hubert Bennett.
111 Exposed concrete. Panels of variably coloured dark bricks. The stair-well pattern derives from additives in the formwork which have a retarding effect. Balcony parapets of cast glass with handrails of clear varnished wood.
112 Exposed concrete. End façades in relief facing brick. Panels of the rear walls of the balconies partly of naturally anodised corrugated aluminium, partly of compound slabs with a layer of red plastic. The balconies have a steel frame construction and the balustrades are of decorative armoured glass.
113 End façades of brown, surface textured precast concrete panels: inserted into these by hand are broken pieces of bottle glass. Cladding panels on the rear walls of the balconies are white with a porcelain material giving an effect of glass. Window frames are black with white casements.
Å Hubert Bennett

114 (Page 67) Blocks of flats in Rome. Walls in yellow and red facing brick. Balconies, roof terrace frames and gutter boards in concrete painted with a rubber-base paint in various contrasting but harmonizing colours.

ᛉ Costa, Parisi, Pfannmüller

115 Combined flats and shops in Rome. Structural walls clad with surface textured precast concrete. Window and door frames of naturally anodised aluminium.

ᛉ Dr Santa de Sanctis

116 Group of flats in Rome. Exposed concrete frame; made up wall panels of bricks. Window wall units of white-glossed timber framework with spandrel and blind box claddings of enamelled asbestos cement slabs (Eternit Glasal). Roof-terrace parapet of exposed concrete.

ᛉ M. Fiorentino

116

117

117 Blocks of owner-occupier flats in Rome. The constructional and form giving details of the two neighbouring buildings vary. Some wall surfaces clad with brick. Continuous balcony parapets and undersides white; balcony structure painted a coal colour with a rubber-base paint. Other balcony balustrades are of decorative armoured glass. Sliding sunshades of horizontally corrugated iron in steel frames painted with gloss paint.
⅄ Giulio Sterbini

118 Blocks of flats in Rome. Exposed concrete frame painted with mineral paint. Panels of sandblasted facing bricks, infill panels and blind boxes clad with enamelled asbestos cement (Eternit Glasal). Window units of Douglas Fir; static parts white, mobile parts glossed red. Steel-framed front doors also glossed. Roof superstructure clad with painted concrete slabs. Railings on the boundary walls of gloss-painted square-section steel.
⅄ E. Borzi, G. B. and F. Tamburini

118

119

120

121

119 High block of flats in Stuttgart. Brickwork clad with glazed a
unglazed split tiles (Gail). Cantilevering slabs on each storey a
prefabricated balcony parapets painted with a rubber-base pai
Å Jörg Herkomm
120 High block of flats in Karlsruhe. Cladding of the end walls
matt glazed split tiles (Gail), with dark joints. Continuous flo
upstands on the southern façade clad with 24.5 x 12 cm. ceran
split tiles. Balcony parapets, gutter facings and faces of the e
posed floor slabs in painted concrete.
Å Prof. Dr H. D. Rösiger and Günther Seema
121 Block of flats in Wolfsburg. Masonry walls clad with engine
ing brick. Balcony parapets and gutters in concrete. All concre
parts as well as the internal walls of the balconies painted whi
Å Hans Uh
122 High block of flats in Stuttgart. This building was erected t
same way as the example in Fig. 119. End walls likewise cl
with ceramic split tiles (Buchtal). Å Jörg Herkomm

122

123

125

123 Section from a group of flats in Rome. Reinforced concrete frame construction. Walls clad with prefabricated, intrinsically coloured concrete slabs. Compound slabs of the window elements clad with enamelled asbestos cement slabs (Eternit Glasal). Å Mario Fiorentino

124 Section from a group of houses in Neuss. Wall cladding of large sized, intrinsically coloured asbestos cement slabs (Eternit Colorit). Balcony parapets partly of painted concrete panels, partly of timber painted with gloss paint. Rear walls of the balconies painted in dark contrasting colours. Å 'New Home' Düsseldorf
125 High block of flats in Heidelberg. Masonry walls clad with asbestos panels painted in two contrasting tones. Balcony parapets of prefabricated concrete. Å Jörg Herkommer

126

126 Blocks of flats in Stuttgart. Wall surfaces in render finished with fines (building in foreground) and in float render; both painted with a rubber-base paint (Caporal). The symmetrically arranged balconies painted white form a contrast; parapets partly of asbestos cement slabs.

Ä Oskar Schwarz and Ernst Bothe

127 High block of flats near Stuttgart. External wall in hollow blocks amongst various prefabricated concrete parts. Wall cladding and window spandrels of asbestos cement slabs (Eternit) painted in two contrasting tones. Front faces of the exposed floor slabs and the balcony parapets are painted.

Ä Jörg Herkommer

128 Section from a high block of flats in Berlin. External walls clad with precast face textured concrete slabs. The balcony parapets are of ceramic mosaic and they form strong colour accents (red, blue and yellow). Windows gloss-painted white.

Ä Van den Broek and Bakema

127

128

129

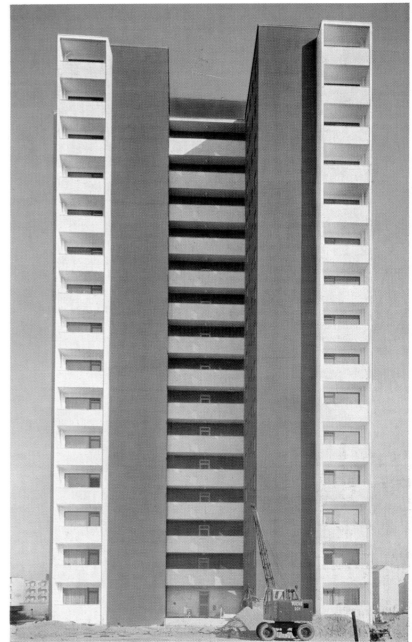

130

129 High block of flats in Birsfelden/Switzerland. Rendered external wall surfaces painted with a rubber-base paint (Sax-Farben). Front parapets of balcony of a contrasting colour. The orange-red sun blinds form yet another contrast.   ⅋ René A. Herter

130 High block of flats in Berlin. All the external walls (mainly prefabricated elements) clad with small ceramic unglazed mosaic (18 x 18 mm.); main surfaces are blue, other parts white. Balcony parapets are clad with 45 x 133 mm. white glazed corrugated panels (Buchtal) and are deployed in vertical half-brick width bands (see detail picture of the street façade).
                                                    ⅋ Planning Department of the Gehag, Berlin

130a

131 High block of flats in Stuttgart. External wall rendered entirely in float render and painted with a rubber-base paint (Diamant). Cladding of the balcony parapets of aluminium roofing sheets with hammer-beaten surface. Roof gutter boards in exposed concrete.

ʎ Otto Traber and Richard Dippon

132 Cluster point blocks with linking stair wells in Copenhagen. Panelled prefabricated concrete elements coloured dark grey; façade divisions a light contrasting colour.

ʎ Ole Buhl

131

132

133 A complex of dwellings in Massy Antony/France. Blank external walls clad with small ceramic mosaic (2 x 2 cm.). Infill panels and blind box covers in enamelled steel sheets. The wooden slatted roller shutters are contrastingly clear-varnished. Exposed parts of the concrete frame painted with a rubber-base paint.
Å Mery and Bocquillon

133

134

135

134 High blocks of flats in Cologne. Solid wall construction, painted with a rubber-base paint (Diwagolan) in three different main colours. The horizontal patterns on the balcony parapets give an enlivening effect. Å Herbert Neubert

135 High blocks of flats in Erlangen. End façades clad with large-sized asbestos cement slabs (Eternit). Continuous spandrels and parapets clad with enamelled asbestos cement panels (Eternit Glasal). The natural colour of the wood of the slatted roller blinds forms a contrast to these. Å Hans Maurer

136 High blocks of flats in Pantin/France. The blocks are built up from large panels and are clad with small ceramic mosaic (5 x 5 cm.). Joints and roof gutters in exposed conc
Å Ai

137 Housing group in Biel/Switzerland. All the concrete surfaces are painted with Muresko paint. The uniform sun blinds — yellow on the high block and red on the low block — pro
strong colour accents. Balcony parapets partly in ornamental armoured glass.
Å Schi

138 Section from a block of flats on a star-shaped ground plan in Milan. Untreated concrete skeleton with facing brick panels. Openwork balcony balustrades of square-section steel, g
painted. Aluminium Venetian blinds.

136

137

138

139

140

139a

139 Blocks of flats in Meaux/France. The concrete external wall slabs
clad in two colours of small ceramic mosaic (5 x 5 cm.) in such a
that the overall effect is decorative and broken up. Side façades
front faces of the reinforced concrete skeleton painted white wi
rubber-base paint.

Ⱥ Jean Ginsberg, Louis Marceau, Schultz van Treeck, Andre J

140 High block of flats in Berlin. Concrete surfaces and dividing eler
painted with a rubber-base paint. Panels on the balcony façades clad
white glazed split tiles. Balcony parapets clad with glass mosaic (Ro
Ⱥ Prof. Klaus Müller-

141 (Page 79) Residential development 'Zollhaus' in a park in Nuremberg. Structural walls. End façades in exposed engineering bricks. Longitudinal façades rendered and painted with a bluish-green rubber-base paint.   Å G. G. Dittrich

142 Prototype building 'Am Dodeshaus' in Osnabrück. One-storey entrance buildings with a door gloss-painted in two colours. Vertical timber planking of the larger, external, door also glossed.   Å Dr O. Dellemann

143 Residential area of Nuremberg-Langwasser. Terrace of one-family houses with façade walls in yellow facing brick with dark joints. Recessed walls rendered with three layers and painted with a blue rubber-base paint. Windows and doors are gloss-painted white.   Å Planning Group Scherzer/Fink

144 Prototype building at Hemmingen-Westerfeld near Hanover. Bearing walls in facing brick. Vertical timber boarding of the upper floors painted with oil paint. Window and door frames white, door itself gloss-painted in various colours.   Å Dr O. Dellemann

145 Estate 'In den Siebenstücken' in Hanover. Facing brickwork with stone-coloured pointing. The slightly recessed external walls of the staircase are rendered and painted with a rubber-base paint. Window and door frames gloss-painted white, the door being clear-varnished.

Å Dr O. Dellemann, Seewald, Lichtenhahn

142

143

144

145

146

147

146 Residential area of Nuremberg-Langwasser. End façades in facing brick, longitudinal façades rendered with three layers of smooth render and painted with a rubber-base paint (Indula). Gutter coverings of asbestos cement. Timber of the recessed entrance gloss-painted; windows the same colour.
Å Planning Group Scherzer/Fink

147 Residential development 'Zollhaus' in a park in Nuremberg. Walls partly of engineering br... partly rendered and painted with a rubber-base paint (Amphibolin). Low parts of the building emphasized in various colours, gutter boards uniformly a contrasting white.   Å G. G. Ditt...

148 and 149 Residential area of Nuremberg-Langwasser. Bearing skeleton of concrete elements. Panelled walls with moderately rough scratched render. Front faces of the exposed concrete floor slabs, gutter facings and balcony parapets painted with a mineral paint (Keim). Claddings of enamelled steel sheet. The horizontal timber claddings form a contrast to these. Projecting, blank stair-well walls of facing brick.   Å Reichel and Hennig

150 Residential development 'Zollhaus' in a park in Nuremberg. Structural walls rendered with three coats of float render and painted with a rubber-base paint (Amphibolin).   Å G. G. Dittrich
151 Prototype building 'Am Dodeshaus' in Osnabrück. Walls of facing brick, with light coloured joints. Coverings to gutters, concrete elements and windows a contrasting white.
Å Dr O. Dellemann

148 and 149

150

151

152

152 Group of houses in Bry-sur-Marne/Fra
Rendered gable walls and balcony parapet
also front faces of the exposed concrete f
slabs painted with a rubber-base paint (Branc
Between the balcony parapets there are lin
panels of hardened glass. On the ground fl
vertical timber boarding and sliding shutters
clear-varnished.   Å Mich
153 Paul-Haertz Estate in Berlin-Charlottenb
The block in the foreground was constructe
a proprietary concrete system (Allbeton)
painted with a rubber-base paint. Balcony p
pets of asbestos cement elements painted wh
The masonry buildings in the background
faced with intrinsically coloured hydraulic
ders. Colour scheme by Prof. G. Janssen.
    Å Prof. Wils Ebert, Prof. W. Weber, F. Ga
154 Section from a block in the residential q
ter 'Am Hasenbergl' in Munich. Rendered r
onry painted with a rubber-base paint. Wine
spandrels in contrasting colours. Parapets
undersides of the balconies painted white.

155

156

157

155 Municipal estate in Chambéry/France. Reinforced structural concrete frame, exposed parts painted white or grey. Within the frame upstand panels in hard wood frames with covering layers of white or grey enamelled asbestos cement panels (Eternit-Glasal).

ᴀ Roger Berthe, Laurent Chappis, Pierre Jomain

156 Residential quarter in Hilversum/Holland. End façades and stair-well walls as also panels on the ground-floor plinth clad with brick. Masonry panel parts on the upper floors rendered and painted in a contrasting colour. Exposed parts of reinforced concrete frame and the concrete balcony parapets painted white. Window spandrel elements of coloured glass (Detopak). ᴀ Hartmann and Eylers

157 Residential area in Badhoevedorp/Holland. Cross walls of brick. Infill elements of the timber-framed windows in a variety of coloured glass (Detopak).

ᴀ Maaskant

158 Henkel Estate 'Kamper Acker'. a—d) reinforced concrete skeleton and gable boards rendered and painted white. Timber work impregnated with a dark colour. Brick panels painted red, blue, yellow or green. e) external walls clad with Dutch bricks. Plinth in painted render. Gutter boards and balcony planking in pine, treated with clear varnish. All the paints used in this complex were rubber-base (Miropan).

Å E. Petersen and W. Köngeter (a—d), Wilms (e)

159 Block of flats with its own shops in 'Am Hasenbergl' Munich. Reinforced concrete construction with rendered masonry panels. Main façade symmetrically divided by various colours of paint. Roof parapet, sides of the gable walls and balcony parapets a contrasting white. The woodwork and the gloss-painted steel construction of the shopping arcade form a powerful contrast to the colours on the high block.

Å E. Hürlimann

158

159

160 The residential quarter 'Am Hasenbergl' in Munich. Composite structure. Masonry external walls rendered and painted with a rubber-base paint. Balcony parapets of prefabricated concrete elements, also painted. The alternation of colours underlines the architectural division. Whilst in the illustration above, a building in the same area as this, the colour division is mainly achieved through paint, here this divisioning also corresponds to the contrasts in the plastic surface structure of the render (the window spandrels in the surface relief lie further back than the adjacent external walls). Colour scheme by W. Torsten.   Å H. Groethuysen

160

161

162

163

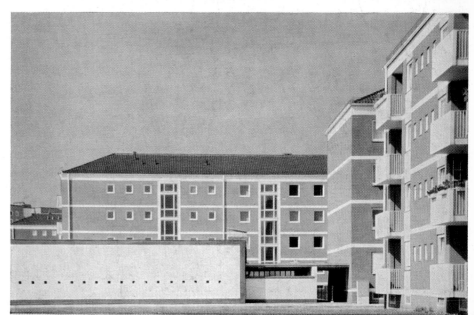

The illustrations on the following pages all show buildings in the 'Fürstenried' quarter of Munich. The colour scheme is by Karl Josef Nerud. Throughout the whole estate only a few colours of pastel tones are used which consequently produce harmonious blends whatever the viewing angle. The entire architectonic structure is prominently contrasted through the floor bands, gutter facings and balcony balustrades, as well as many of the gable façades, being painted white. The external walls are painted with a rubber-base paint (161—163 Diwagolan). The staggered heights of the buildings are emphasized by, amongst other things, the one-storey garage blocks being painted not only white but also being multi-coloured.

161 Blocks of flats each of which forms a square with two through-ways on one side. Ӑ Hans Knapp-Schachleiter

162 View through a terrace-house quarter towards a cluster block. Ӑ Franz Ruf

163 Primary School. Exposed concrete and rendered areas painted with a rubber-base paint. Steel columns glossed blue. Rear wall of the walkway is red. Inserted ceramic tiles, flush with the render, by Kay Krasnitzky. Ӑ Georg Roemmich

164 Free-standing blocks, each of which has two lower garage courts connected one with the other; in front of each of these, two rows of garages are arranged. Whilst the multicoloured tones were continued on the flats, the main surfaces of the garages were kept a light colour.

Ӑ Ernst Hürlimann and Hans Knapp-Schachleiter

165

166

165 Further illustration from the 'Fürstenried' quarter in Munich: slightly staggered blocks of flats in alternating tones. End façades, gutter facings and horizontal bands at floor levels are white float render; remaining wall surfaces in coloured float render (Terranova).   Ⓐ Ernst Maria Lang
166 Blocks of flats linked by recessed stair wells. On the end façade of the main building a projecting stair well which terminates the corridors. In the main, only the longitudinal façades show the main tone of the paint (Diwagolan). Picture 166 a reproduces a section from the front façade of the blocks   Ⓐ Ernst Maria Lang

167

167 Blocks of flats whose end façades and balcony parapets on the longitudinal facades are kept light whilst the colour emphasis on the front façades changes from block to block. For every block there is a two-storey garage unit which has no multi-coloured accents.

Ʌ Ernst Maria Lang

168 High blocks of flats with party walls of exposed prefabricated concrete. End façades clad with sawn conglomerate stone. Balcony parapets of aluminium sheet glossed white. In the one storey block in the foreground there are a post office and a credit bank.

Ʌ Prof. Fred Angerer

166a

168

169 Section from a block of flats in the 'Am Hasenbergl' estate in Munich. The wall mural on the stair block was done in rubber-base paints (Indula) by Willy Torsten. It contrasts with the light coloured horizontal divisioning of the building. 169a shows a variation.

ᚦ New Home Bavaria

169

169a

171 Detail of a block in the 'Am Hasenbergl' estate in Munich. The rendered and painted areas are divided up light horizontal bands at floor level: a rubber-base paint is used. Window infill panels and linteis are the tone of the recessed stair-well walls. Ⓐ Gordon Ludwig and Franz Raab

and 172 Buildings in the 'Am Harthof' estate in Munich. Rendered areas painted with a rubber-base paint. Here also the architectonic structure is underlined through the symmetrical provisioning by means of white paint. Ⓐ Friedrich Haindl

173

173 Blocks of flats in Basle. Rendered areas painted with a rubber-base paint. Walls on the ground floor clad with engineering bricks. Balcony balustrades of coloured armoured glass. Square box section hangers which carry the balustrades and balcony slabs are glossed black. The orange-red sun blinds form a regular colour accent. Ⓐ Suter & Suter
174 Blocks in the residential quarter of 'Neue Vahr' in Bremen. Structural walls, rendered and painted with Muresko. End walls and recessed wall areas coloured, balcony walls white. Balcony parapets clad with engineering bricks. Ⓐ Dr Säume, G. Hafemann, Dr Reichow, Prof. May

174

176

177

175 (Page 93) Home for young people in Silberborn/Uslar. The building is sited on a slope and is clad with vertical timber boarding, colour impregnated. Walls of the common rooms of timber frame construction and asbestos cement compound slabs (Eternit), blue externally and white internally. Chimmey in quarry stone. Gutter coverings, timber framework and windows treated with white gloss. Sun blinds are a harmonizing colour.

Ꙗ Witte, Brettschneider, Lessing, Kärst
176 Youth hostel in Urach/Württemberg. Reinforced concrete frame closed with hollow block walling, external walls clad partly with vertical timber and partly with Gauinger non-calcerous tufa. Window spandrels on the end façade rendered and painted with mineral paint.

Ꙗ Willy Bailmann and Werner Stähle
177 Children's home in the holiday village 'Corte di Cadore' near Cortina d'Ampezzo/Italy. Reinforced concrete frame with bearing end walls of roughly mortared quarry stone. Rendered panels painted with two bright colours. Snow timber roof with sheet covering.

Ꙗ Dr Eduardo Gellner

178

178 Youth hostel in Milan. Rendered walls painted with a rubber-base paint. Projecting roof gutter boards and exposed concrete floor slabs in a contrasting light colour. The walkways in front of the dormitories are screened off with walls of brick, fretwork, elements.   Å Mario Righini

179 Home for young people of the protestant parish in Hagen near Lage/Lippe. Rendered external walls of both parts of the building painted in three colours. Light metal windows (Schürmann).   Å Karl Gerke

179

180

180 Home for young people with gymnasium in Stuttgart-Mühlhausen. Upper floor of the home is clad with slabs of engineering-type brick (Buchtal). Ground floor and gymnasium float rendered, painted with a rubber-base paint. Gutters in exposed concrete.

Ⓐ Main Building Authorities of Stuttgart

181 Students' Hostel for the State School of Building Engineers in Aachen. Reinforced concrete skeleton with panels of pumice stone masonry. External wall claddings: light metal profile frames with enamelled asbestos cement compound slabs (Eternit Glasal) in two colours. Balcony parapets of concrete painted with white mineral paint. The black-and-white illustrations show the rear view of the building and the lower structure containing the communal rooms which forms a light-coloured contrast to the main building. Ⓐ Prof. Dr Winter and Heinen

181

182

183

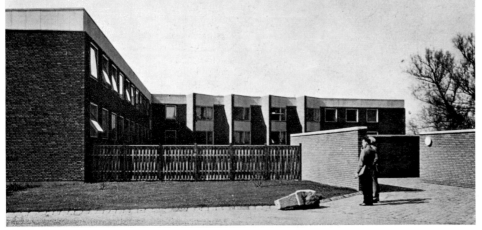

184

182 Students' Hostel of the Technical University of Berlin. Rendered walls painted. Plinth, front faces of the exposed floor slabs and gutters a contrasting dark colour. Timber windows glossed white, with infill panels of enamelled asbestos cement (Eternit Glasal). Ⓐ Peter Lehrecke

183 Flats for nurses in the Aggertal Hospital in Engelskirchen. Walls clad with engineering type bricks (Teeuwen). Balcony parapets and roof superstructures clad with slate. Windows and doors of wood glossed white.
    Ⓐ Prof. Harald Deilmann
184 Hostel in Bogense/Denmark. Bearing facing brickwork with dark joints. Gutter facings and window spandrels of grey asbestos cement slabs.
    Ⓐ Salling-Mortensen

185 Nursing home for the elderly in Seehau
Upper Bavaria. Bearing walls in pumice
brick, rendered and painted with a rubber-ba
paint (Diwagolan). Continuous balcony para
in concrete. Stair well in 'Profilit' glass.
Ⓐ Robert Reu

186 Personnel and trainee nurses' block of
University children's hospital in Heidelb
Reinforced concrete skeleton, painted g
Panels in yellow facing brick. White-glos
timber window-frames, with dark grey ename
spandrels. Ⓐ Albrecht Lange and Hans Mitz
187 Students' Hostel in Karlsruhe. Brick struct
walls, flush jointed and painted in three colo
with a rubber-base paint (Akalin). Balcony p
pets in white-painted exposed concrete.
Ⓐ Prof. Rudolf Büchner and Klaus Ba

185

186

187

188

188 Nurses' Hostel in England. Bearing reinforced concrete frame. External walls in timber frame construction with asbestos cement compound elements (Eternit). The front faces of the floors and columns are also clad with asbestos cement slabs. Panels on the ground floor in facing brick

Å S. G. Besant Roberts

189 Hostel for construction workers in Le Levassay/France. Walls of upper floors clad with timber. Window spandrels of the lower floors in white enamelled asbestos cement slabs (Eternit Glasal). Å A. Remondet, A. Malizard, A. Serraz

189

190

190 Hostel for single people in Grand-Charmont near Sochaux/France. Exposed concrete structure. Panelled window walls of enamelled asbestos cement compound elements in two colours (Eternit Glasal).   Å J. Fállou

191 Hostel in Kilchmatt near Muttenz/Switzerland. Structural walls clad with facing brick. Concrete balcony parapets and the cladding of the pergola-like roof superstructure painted with rubber-base paint.

192 Hostel in Frankfurt/Main. Structural walls clad with facing bricks. Loggia and balcony parapets and window lintels of prefabricated concrete elements.   Å Krauss and Schlüter

191   192

193

194

193 Hotel in the mountains/Japan. Reinforced concrete frame. The external walls of the stair tower are clad with diagonal rows of bricks. Exposed parts of the frame and the rendered areas are white, underside of the roof extension painted red. Balcony balustrades of concrete slabs and black-glossed square-section steel. Å Masachika Murata

195 Detail from a holiday hotel in Jesolo/Pineta/Italy. The panels in the reinforced concrete skeleton are partly colour rendered and partly formed with an exposed concrete relief. Å Renzo Men

194 Section of a family hotel in the Savoy. Reinforced concrete frame. End walls in exposed concrete. Window façades of timber framework. The sandwich slabs of the infill panels are clad internally with smooth, enamelled asbestos cement (Eternit) and externally with the same, but rough, material (Eternit). Å M. Pradel

196 Hotel in Stuttgart. The structural walls are clad externally entirely with light grey marble. The blue window infills, the red sandstone terraces of the external gardens as well as the sunblinds, form colour contrasts. Å Hans Paul Schmohl

195

196

197

197 Hotel in the holiday village 'Corte di Cadore' near Cortina d'Ampezzo/Italy (see also illustration no. 177). Reinforced concrete skeleton with bearing walls in quarry stone masonry. Panels in brick, rendered and painted in two colours. Front faces of the floor slabs, entrance porch and chimney in exposed concrete, painted. Timber of the balcony balustrades and of the roof extension colour impregnated. Windows white-glossed.   Ⱥ Dr Eduardo Gellner

198 Hotel in Andros/Greece. Unrendered reinforced concrete frame and rendered areas of the brickwork panels painted with mineral paint. Infill masonry of the ground floor in quarry stone. Metal parts glossed grey-green. The illustration on the right shows a section of the building.   Ⱥ Aris Konstantinidis

198

199

200

201

199 Hotel in Kalambaka/Greece. Reinforc
concrete frame, painted grey. Panelled wa
rendered a contrasting white. The walkw
in front of the rooms are terminated
painted Novopan panels. Rods and bal
trades glossed orange. Illustrations no.
show a hotel site in Poros/Greece which
similar in structure and tonal effect to
complex shown in illustration no. 199.

Ѧ Aris Konstantini

201 Hotel in Bad Neustadt/Saale. Reinforc
concrete columns on the two lower floc
cross walls on the three upper floors. W
of brick and foam concrete. Exposed c
crete, rendered areas, and balcony parap
of asbestos cement, painted with a rubb
base paint (Amphibolin). The window faça
of the stair well in ceramic honeycomb.

Ѧ Fritz H

202 Section of the entrance side of the specialist hospital in Bad Salzuflen. Structural walls (of the wards) of engineering bricks. The projecting entrance is clad with glass mosaic. Steel windows, porch roof and balustrade gloss-painted.   Å Prof. Harald Deilmann

203 Wards of the MRC hospital in Hamburg. Reinforced concrete construction with masonry panels. External walls clad with red hard-burnt brick and light-grey glazed ceramic slabs.   Å Prof. Paul Seitz
204 The Aggertal Hospital in Engelskirchen. External walls of the main buildings clad with engineering bricks. Balcony parapets and the adjacent multipurpose hall clad with natural slate. Copper roof and roof cladding. Timber window-frames white-glossed.   Å Prof. Harald Deilmann

202

203

204

205 Municipal and District Hospital, Kulmbach. Reinforced concrete skeleton with brick walls entirely faced with greyish-yellow narrow tiles. Windows coated with colourless varnish.   Å Georg Köhler and Felix Kässens
206 Land Social Welfare (LVA) Kneipp sanatorium in Manderscheid/Eifel. Reinforced concrete skeleton, entirely clad with narrow facing bricks (Gail) in old white, black and light blue.   Å Hoischen

205

108

207

207 The University Dental Hospital in Freiburg/Breisgau. All structure in reinforced concrete. Three-storey treatment department: external walls of the recessed ground floors clad with horizontal timber. The cross bands at floor level are of prefabricated concrete. Window spandrels of terrazzo slabs. Ward block: sun screens and end walls of concrete. Rendered panels painted with a rubber-base paint (Amphibolin). Lecture block (on right of illustration): cladding of silver-grey anodised aluminium profiles. Gutter coverings of prefabricated concrete.   Ⓐ The University Building Authorities II Freiburg

208 Municipal Hospital in Frankfurt/Main-Hoechst. All external walls are clad with split tiles (Buchtal). Over the windows of the main building are sun screens of light metal.   Ⓐ Apel & Beckert, Becker (Main building);
Jack Martin Michel and Klaus Wirth (low buildings)
209 Aggertal Hospital (see also illustration no. 204). The building is entirely clad with yellowish-grey engineering-type bricks. Balcony parapets clad with slate. Windows white-glossed.   Ⓐ Prof. Harald Deilmann

208

209

210

210 The Catherine Hospital in Frankfurt/Main. The light parts of the external wall are clad with panels of small split tiles (Buchtal), the rendered areas between the windows being painted with a rubber-base paint. All the sun blinds are a contrasting blue. The chapel is in facing brick.   Å Giefer and Mäckler
211 Annexe to the District Hospital in Roskilde/Denmark. Structural facing brickwork with the addition of claddings. Windows of brown impregnated timber. Spandrels on the ground floor of asbestos cement slabs painted with latex paint. Bars of galvanised iron.   Å Salling-Mortensen
212 Hospital in Rome. Reinforced concrete skeleton, painted grey. Panels of brick cladding. The exposed concrete divisions between balconies and the rendered areas on the top floor painted with a white rubber-base paint. Balcony balustrades are steel framed with panes of cast glass   Å Attilio Lapadulla
213 (Page 110) Sanatorium in Löwenstein/Württemberg. Reinforced concrete skeleton with panels of Ytong. External walls are all clad with panels of engineering-type brick (Buchtal). Upper balcony parapets and rendered areas of the rear walls of the balconies painted in two colours with a rubber-base paint. Windows and doors in anodised aluminium (Gartner). Vertically running sunblinds in an appropriate colour.   Å G. Köhler and F. Kässens

211

212

214 (Page 111) Primary School Bötelkamp in Hamburg-Lokstedt. Bearing walls in yellow facing brick, flush jointed. Doors and windows of fir, white-glossed. ⋏ Prof. Godber Nissen

215 System building school pavilion in Düsseldorf-Gerresheim. External cladding of the blank areas is Sipo-mahogany boarding, 22 mm. thick and given a coat of high-gloss varnish. Window infill panels of enamelled sheet. Windows and gutter facings gloss-painted. ⋏ A product of the firm of de Groots Houtbouw N. V.

216 Kindergarten in New Ulm/Danube. Blank end façades are faced with engineering bricks. Window walls are electrically welded steel construction with aluminium windows and enamelled panels (Gartner). Harmonizing with these are the green-glossed doors and the yellow curtains. Underside of the roof clad with impregnated timber boards. ⋏ Building Authorities of New Ulm.

215

216

217

217 School pavilion shown on the occasion of an exhibition of system building in Milan. Light steel and aluminium frame construction. External walls of colour anodised aluminium.

218

218 Kindergarten in Milan. The building consists of four equal-sized rooms which are grouped round the central hall. Reinforced concrete frame. Panels of brick cladding. Copper roof.   Å Arrigo Arrighetti

219 Primary school in Bassum/Bremen. Structural walls partly in facing brick and partly rendered and painted with a contrasting coat of a rubber-base paint. Gutters in exposed concrete. Balcony balustrades of dark impregnated boards. Windows are white-glossed.
Å Rolf Störmer
220 Primary School in Rotkreuz/Switzerland. Gable walls and free-standing chimney in facing brick. The linking block is rendered and painted with mineral paint. Supporting walls and window lintels, rough-cast exposed concrete. Doors blue-glossed.　　Å P. Weber

219

220

221

221 School in St Maurice/Switzerland. The complex of one- and two-storey buildings is sited on rising ground. Reinforced concrete construction painted with mineral paint. End walls in natural stone. Panelled linking walls clad with clear-varnished fir.
Å Daniel Girardet
222 Kindergarten in Rockenberg. Bearing external walls of sand-yellow semi-engineering bricks, dark jointed. All timber umber colour impregnated. Window casements white-glossed.
Å Hans Köhler
223 Secondary school in Buchs/Switzerland. Exposed concrete walls on the ground floor, dark grey; rendered brick walls light grey painted with a rubber-base paint. Gables clad with asbestos cement façade slabs (Eternit).
Å Otto Riek

222   223

224

224 Primary and secondary school 'Kamphofer Damm' in Bremen. Bearing reinforced concrete skeleton. Blank end walls clad with split narrow tiles (240 x 52 x 20 mm.). Window infill panels clad with painted asbestos cement slabs (Eternit). Plinth and front faces of the exposed concrete floor slabs rendered and painted with a rubber-base paint. The glazed 'butterfly' form stair-well has an aluminium roof.

Å Rolf Störmer

225

225 Primary school in Dortmund-Rahm. Reinforced concrete skeleton. Cross walls clad with facing engineering bricks. Exposed concrete floor slabs project to give protection from the sun. Infills of white enamelled steel sheet (Salm). Window frames gloss-painted black and white.   Ӓ Prof. Dr F. W. Kraemer

226 Primary school in Düsseldorf. *In situ* reinforced concrete skeleton painted black. Aluminium-framed window units (Erbslöh). Infills of compound slabs with porcelain-enamelled sheet-steel surface. Gable sides of the classroom section clad with ultramarine glazed bricks and on the gymnasium side with orange-red glazed bricks. The internal courtyard is paved with leather-coloured bricks.   Ӓ Prof. Paul Schneider-Esleben

226

227

227 Secondary-modern school in Schongau. Reinforced concrete skeleton painted white. Ground floor clad with natural stone slabs. Rendered spandrels a contrasting dark colour. Aluminium windows, anodised, with proprietary casements (Gartner). Porch in steel with anodised aluminium cladding and clear-varnished boarding on its underside.   Ӿ Josef Schuster

228 School in Triegen/Switzerland. Rendered gable walls, bands of exposed concrete and front faces of the concrete floor slabs in the stair well painted in three different colours of a rubber-base paint (Amphibolin).   Ӿ K. Müller and F. Arnold

229 Linking block of the Karolinen school in Frankenthal/Pfalz. Skeleton in exposed concrete. Panels clad with yellow semi-engineering bricks. Gutter covering light grey, underside of covered way and the windows are painted white. In the covered way there is a fountain of coloured mosaic.   Ӿ Prof. Heinrich Müller

228

229

Section from two system-built schools in France. The entire structure is of steel. External faces are enamelled.

School in Brussels. Reinforced concrete skeleton painted with grey rubber-base paint. Blank gable areas of facing brick. Some timber window-frames are clear-varnished, some are white-glossed. Infills clad with asbestos cement panels (Eternit).

Å Willy Reyns

231

232

233 The Brother and Sister Scholl grammar s
in Düsseldorf. Reinforced concrete frame.
walls of brick, painted various colours w
rubber-base paint (Diwagolan). Window infi
enamelled steel sheet. The panels of the
storey block (on the right of the illustration
vertically boarded with colour impregnated
ber. The school yard and the sports areas
demarcated through three different materials.
Ⅎ Heinz Kale
234 Continuation and evening grammar s
in Dortmund-Brüninghausen. Reinforced conc
boarded face, structure. Blank walls clad
engineering bricks (Gail). Timber window-fr
are inserted within the frame structure and
enamelled steel-sheet infills. Doors are c
varnished. Ⅎ Prof. Dr F. W. Kra

235 Extension to the August-Jaspert scho
Frankfurt-Bonames. In situ concrete frame. C
walls and infill panels clad with 12 x 12 cm.
glazed split tiles (Gail). Stair-well walls of
bricks. Rendered areas between and unde
windows painted. Metal parts glossed dark b
Authorities, Frankfurt/Main.
(see also detail in illustration no. 235 a).
Ⅎ Building Authorities, Frankfurt

232 Grammar school in Königstein/Taunus. Reinforced
concrete skeleton on a module of 4 m. Steel frame
elements containing desk-height infill panels of compound slabs clad with enamelled asbestos cement
(Eternit-Glasal). Blank wall surfaces partly clad with
bricks, partly rendered and painted. Doors are gloss-
painted in various colours.
Ⅎ Rudolf Kramer, Bert Seidel, H. Hausmann

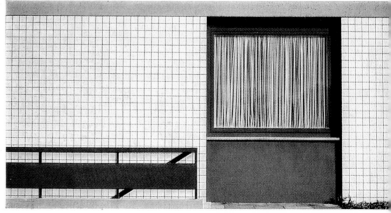

235a

233

234

235

236 Queen Louise School in Cologne. Reinforced concrete skeleton. Cladding partly of white, partly of yellow glazed tiles (Buchtal). Gable walls in the same material but dark blue in colour. Continuous light metal sun shades. Concrete stairwell wall by Prof. Mestermann. Å P. F. Schneider

237 Berta von Suttner school in Essen. Reinforced concrete frame. Spandrel bands clad with 7.1 x 24.5 cm. ceramic tiles (Buchtal). Timber window elements clear-varnished.   Ⱥ Hans Eggeling

238 School in Salierstrasse Düsseldorf-Oberkassel. Reinforced concrete frame. Main walls in red, sand-faced, semi-engineering bricks. Infill panels on the stair well and on the linking block clad with white stone slabs. Window frames glossed either white or black. Continuous aluminium sun screen.   Ⱥ H. Rhode

239 School in Holland. Spandrel bands clad with yellow asbestos cement slabs. The blank, projecting stair-well walls decorated with various coloured concrete blocks (designed by Aalt Roos). Timber framework of the windows white-glossed.   Ⱥ B. J. Odink

237

238

239

240 Grammar school in Stuttg
Zuffenhausen. Reinforced concr
frame. End walls clad with
engineering bricks in a distinc
pattern. Infills in floated scratc
render. Window frames white-gl
ed. ∧ Building Authorities of Stutt
241 Luise-Schröder High School
Munich. Reinforced concrete fra
Brick panels; partly exposed, pa
clad with narrow tiles or rende
and painted with a rubber-b
paint. Upper gutter covering
copper. Window frames glos
white.   ∧ Ernst Maria L

240

242 Hebel Grammar School
Schwetzingen. Reinforced conc
frame. Front faces of the floor sl
of shaped, exposed concrete
ments. Infills of enamelled s
sheet. Windows in timber and
minium. Steel structure of the
vered entrance gloss-painted.
∧ Hirsch, Hoinkis, Lanz, Schütz, S

242

243 Assembly Hall of the Clara Schumann school in Düsseldorf. Reinforced concrete clad with Dutch engineering bricks. Light metal ventilation lamellas taken up to the edge of the gutter boards. Timber of the doors and windows glossed white.

⅄ Building Authorities Düsseldorf

243

244

245

Vilhelms Grammar School in Stuttgart-Degerloch.
orced concrete skeleton. Solid parts of facing
engineering bricks. Infills of profiled asbestos
nt slabs (Eternit). Plinth clad with ridged con-
slabs. Windows glossed white.
 Å Prof. Hans Volkart

ade School at Kreuzlingen. Bearing external walls
posed sandstone in a decorative fashion. Spand-
lad with aluminium coated and enamelled sheet
(Emalco). See also both the detail illustrations
e right. Å Edwin Schoch

aining block of the shopkeeper's union in Basle.
orced concrete frame painted white. Continuous
of coloured render. Å Suter & Suter
ade School in Heilbronn *In situ* concrete skel-
painted. Infill panels clad with 25 x 12 cm.
d ceramic tiles (Buchtal). Windows glossed
v. Å Baer, Dr Gabel, Hieber

246

247

248

246 Day continuation school in Si
Switzerland. Reinforced concrete co
truction. In front of the main façade th
is a metal curtain wall with vertical al
inium sliding windows and infill pan
of asbestos cement slabs (Eternit). On
ground floor, recessed glazing wit
shaped concrete elements.
Ⓐ Morisod, Kyburz, Fu

249 Trade school in Sion/Switzerla
Exposed concrete construction, paint
Blank end walls on the ground floor
facing brick. Window wall units of anodis
aluminium. Rendered infill panels pain
with a rubber-base paint. External st
in precast face textured concrete.
Ⓐ Pierre Schr

249

250

250 School of engineering in Giessen. Main building in reinforced concrete, with exposed shuttering on the external walls. The adjacent building is constructed of steel which is gloss-painted. Panels of both buildings clad with engineering bricks (Dörentrup).   Ⱥ Ministry of Works, Giessen
251 Hedwig-Heyl vocational school in Berlin-Charlottenburg. Reinforced concrete construction. End walls in facing brick. Horizontal bands clad with vertical strips of light and dark narrow split tiles (Buchtal).
Ⱥ Building Authorities of Berlin-Charlottenburg

251a

251

252

252a

253

253a

254a

254

252 Vocational school in Frechen near Cologne. Reinforced concrete frame. Longitudinal walls panelled with narrow facing bricks, the end walls with profiled glazed ceramic tiles (Buchtal). Design: Rolf Crummenauer. ⋏ F. Steeg and H. Schnieders
253 The Physics and Chemistry block of the School of Engineering in Karlsruhe. Reinforced concrete frame; externally exposed concrete. Infill elements of enamelled steel sheets. Blank end walls have an exposed concrete relief by Erich Hauser. (See detail illustration no. 253a). ⋏ Municipal Building Authorities of Karlsruhe

254 An advanced training school for tradesmen in Düsseldorf. Reinforced concrete skeleton; faces painted with a rubber-base paint. (The illustration on the right shows its appearance in cloudy weather.) Infill panels clad with split tiles (Buchtal). Windows and doors blue-glossed. ⋏ Heinz Kalenborn
255 State engineering school in Furtwangen. Reinforced concrete frame. Vertical, recessed, timber boarding on the window infill panels painted red, windows glossed white.

255

256

257

256 Club rooms on a sports field. Bearing wa[ll]
in facing brick. Roof constructed in timb[er]
Painted surfaces: cashier's office grey, wind[ow]
wall white, doors red, opening lights bl[ue]
roof cantilevers brown.   Ꜹ B.J. Od[e]
257 Hall for indoor games in a Primary Schoo[l]
Munich. Bearing construction of exposed c[on]
crete. End walls clad with engineering bric[k.]
The remaining surfaces are painted with [a]
rubber-base paint in colours to harmonize w[ith]
the bricks.   Ꜹ Sepp Pog[t]

258

258 Gymnasium of a mining school in Niederrhein. Steel frame construction (Gartner), gloos-painted an anthracite colour. Panels either of glass brick or of facing brick. Ѧ Heinz Thoma
259 Sports centre of an industrial concern in Marl. Frame in steel and reinforced concrete. Panelled end walls clad with intrinsically coloured concrete slabs. Rendered infill panels painted with synthetic Kautschuk-Latex paint. Steel windows painted alternately yellow and white. Ѧ Prof. Walter Henn

259

260

260 Stadium in Essen. Construction: reinforced concrete trestles, timber roof beams in the Hetzer building method laminated timber tie rods in steel. Access to the covered stands in exposed concrete. Stairs of prefabricated reinforced concrete elements. Timber balustrades, clear-varnished, on composite steel sections. The hall walls are partly of facing brick and partly vertically boarded with timber.   Ⱥ Ulrich S. von Altenstadt (Stand) and Ernst von Rudloff (Hall)

261 Indoor swimming pool in Mainz. The hall is a compound structure of steel supports and white-painted exposed concrete. The front structure: blank walls clad with black glazed split tiles.   Ⱥ Otto Apel, Hannsgeorg Beckert, Gilbert Becker

261

262 Institute of Mechanical Processing of the Technical High School, Karlsruhe. Reinforced concrete frame. Blank end walls in facing engineering bricks. Window infill panels clad with glazed tiles. Å Building Authorities of the Higher Education Department, Karlsruhe

263

263 An academy of arts in Berlin. External walls in exposed aggregate concrete with the addition of white marble pebbles. Exposed masonry of Dutch, handpainted bricks, timber of the window wall glossed white. External walls of the higher level buildings are rendered with a moderately grainy scratched float render. The roof coverings are copper. Å Prof. Werner Düttmann

264 Institute of Hydraulics and water economics of the Technical High School, Berlin. Reinforced concrete skeleton painted with a rubber-base paint. Panels clad with unglazed split tiles (240/51). High level band of windows in Profilit glazing; the ventilation louvres above these are of steel sheet painted with oil paint.

264

5

266

268

5 Detail of one of the institutes of the Technical High School of
Berlin. Dark joints to the horizontal or vertical brick cladding.
6 Institute of High Voltage Techniques at the Technical High School,
Munich. Reinforced concrete wall surfaces entirely clad in facing
bricks.   Ᾱ Prof. Werner Eichberg and Prof. Franz Hart

267 Academy of Pedagoguey in Freiburg. Skeleton of prefabricated concrete elements. Panels clad in
part with precast, black face, textured concrete slabs and in part rendered and painted.
268 Institute of the Technology and Application of Gas and of Water Chemistry at the Technical High
School, Karlsruhe. Buildings erected in reinforced concrete frame construction. Panels in facing engineering
bricks (Lüngen). Windows and doors glossed white.
                    Ᾱ The Building Authorities of the Higher Education Department of Karlsruhe

269

270

269 Training school for Management Sciences in Speyer. Walls of the upper floor clad with split tiles (Buchtal). Recessed ground floor likewise clad with ceramic slabs. Balcony parapets of asbestos cement. Front faces of the exposed concrete floor slabs painted green.

ᚠ Prof. Sep Ruf

270 Institute of Electrotechnology of the Technical High School, Karlsruhe. The buildings are entirely clad with engineering bricks 240 x 52 x 52 cm. Windows of light metal.

ᚠ Prof. Rudolf Büchner and Zimmermann

271 Institute for the construction of agricultural machines and aeroplanes at the Technical High School, Brunswick. Reinforced concrete skeleton, painted grey. Infill panels of polished precast face textured slabs, manufactured with a white-coloured cement (Dyckerhoff). End walls clad with brick. Saw roof building: ground floor clad with panels of hard-burnt brick, gables painted brickwork.

ᚠ New Building Authorities of the Technical High School, Brunswick

272 A State Cold Store for foodstuffs in Karlsruhe. Reinforced concrete frame, painted. Upstands clad with split tiles. Infill panels of the link block of asbestos cement slabs (Eternit) and painted with a rubber-base paint. Timber framework of the windows gloss-painted.

ᚠ State Building Authorities II, Karlsruhe

271

272

272a

273 Institute of Forensic Medicine of the University of Freiburg. Reinforced concrete frame. Panels of yellow facing brick. Sun shades of prefabricated concrete elements. ⋀ University Building Authorities I, Freiburg
274 Phillips Academy in Andover, Mass/USA. Bearing structure of reinforced concrete, painted. Wall slabs clad in facing brick. ⋀ Prof. Walter Gropius

275 Institute of Waltham University Mass/USA. Frame of reinforced concrete, painted. Blank walls of facing brick. Steel window-frames gloss-painted. Gutters covered with painted prefabricated concrete elements. ⋀ Benjamin Thompson
276 Radiology Institute of the University of Freiburg. Reinforced concrete frame; cladding panels of yellow engineering bricks. ⋀ University Building Authorities I, Freiburg
277 Laboratory for Applied Physics at the Technical High School of Munich. Boarded reinforced concrete frame. Facing bricks. ⋀ Prof. Franz Hart and Prof. Josef Wiedemann

273

274

275

276

277

279a

278

279

280

278 Institute of Law and Economics at the University of Mainz. Wall surfaces between the windows clad with panels of split tiles (Gail). Infill panels rendered and painted with a blue rubber-base paint. Front faces of the exposed concrete floor slabs a contrasting white. Metal parts glossed black.

Ⱥ Lenz Architects and Engineers

279 Eastern Europe and Otto-Suhr Institute at the University of Berlin. Bearing reinforced concrete frame. Walls on the ground floor clad with grey, small ceramic mosaic (see detail illustration no. 279a). Upper-floor walls clad with the same material, but in blue. Compound panels painted white form the upstands.

Ⱥ Senate for the control of Building and Housing in Berlin

280 Max Planck Institute of Nuclear Physics in Heidelberg. The whole building is clad with dark jointed narrow tiles. Windows of anodised aluminium.

Ⱥ Lange and Mitzlaff

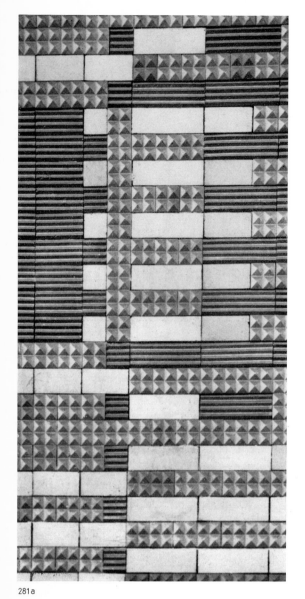

281a

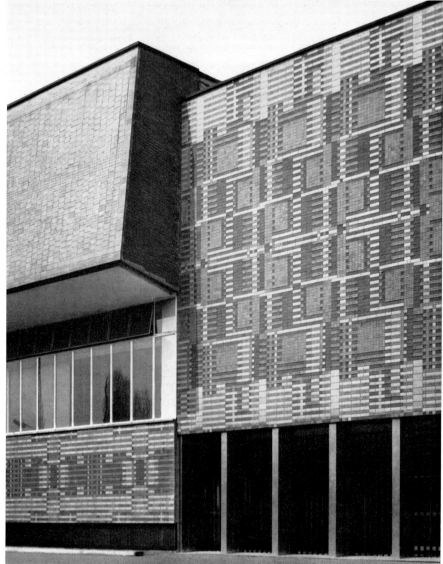

281

282

Institute of the University of Milan. Walls clad with coarse
amic elements. Slabs in three different tones of brown with
ering formats and reliefs (see detail picture 281a). Columns
he entrance have a light metal cladding.   ⋀ Giordano Forti
Institute Buildings with Lecture Theatre at the Technical
School, Karlsruhe. Lecture hall clad with glazed ceramic
os, other buildings in reinforced concrete with panels of
ng engineering bricks.

uilding Authorities of the Higher Education Department,
Karlsruhe

Philosophy Faculty of the University of Hamburg. Structure
he high blocks is exposed concrete, painted. Infill panels
end walls clad with split tiles (Gail). Walls of the one-
ey areas clad with marble. Window wall frames and
ers white-glossed.   ⋀ Prof. Paul Seitz
Institute of the University of Milan. The whole building is
with zigzag rows of glazed narrow tiles. The structural
nbers divide up the façade and, together with the project-
window frames, are clad with light metal.   ⋀ Gio Ponti

283

284a

285 Institute of Nuclear Physics at the Technical High School, Darmstadt. The complex consists of a basic core with a large experiments room, workshops, laboratories and lecture room and four-storey laboratory block. All the buildings are clad with a medium-sized mosaic (5 x 5 cm). Window frames are light metal. Ⲁ State Building Authorities, Darmstadt

286 Variations on a similar form of cladding to that in example no. 285 (An electrotechnical centre in Frankfurt/Main). Wall surfaces clad with ceramic mosaic 10 x 10 cm. Doors glossed blue. See also illustrations 436 and 436a. Ⲁ Otto Apel

285

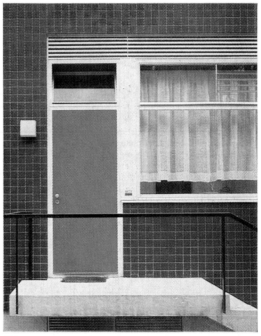

286

285a

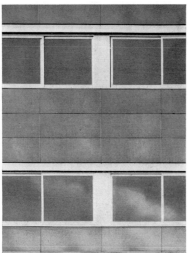

287

287 Physical Institute of the University of Giessen. Reinforced concrete frame. Curtain wall facade of 162.5 x 62.5 cm. enamelled steel sheets (Salm). Aluminium sliding windows, naturally anodised. (The building was photographed from the roof of a lower block whose infill panels are similarly fabricated enamelled steel sheets.)

Å State University Building Authority, Giessen

288

289

288 Institute of the Technical University of Berlin. Rein[
concrete frame painted light grey. Infill panels of crystal
glass which on one side is sprayed blue. Aluminium w[
frames. Plinth of the lower block clad with bricks.
ⴷ Prof. Wilhelm [

289 Staff block of the department of chemical technolog[
physical chemistry at the Technical High School of Brun[
Bearing frame in reinforced concrete. Continuous upstand
clad with glazed and unglazed small ceramic mosaic (2 x 2
Front façade of the projecting, glazed stair well clad[
bricks. Window frames glossed white, casements dark grey
ⴷ New Building Authorities of the Technical High School, Bru[

290 Institute of Inorganic Chemistry at the Technical University, Berlin. Main building: blank walls clad with light grey glass mosaic. Infill panels and blind box covers of glass (Opal). Front façade of staircase block of glass bricks. Walls of the lower blocks (290 on the right and 290a) clad with brick. Plinth and front faces of the exposed concrete floor slabs painted with a white rubber-base paint. Upper floor of the lecture hall (illustration 290b) clad with split tiles; the joints to these are dark and so divide up the façade.

Ⓐ Building Department of the University of Berlin

290

290a

290b

291

291a

292

292a

293

School of Economics and Sociology in St Gallen. All the buildings, including the supporting walls, staircases, surrounds to the
flower beds etc., are in exposed concrete. Window walls have a
steel construction, gloss-painted. ⋀ Förderer, Otto and Zwimpfer

Protestant Academy in Mülheim/Ruhr. Visitors' block: cross walls
in front of which are prefabricated steel frames containing windows,
wall panels and balcony doors. Parapets of painted asbestos cement
compound slabs. Lecture block: steel frame construction painted
dark colour. Side façades have a combined fitting which protects
against sun. Blank end wall in exposed concrete.
⋀ Prof. F. G. Winter

Physical Institute of the University of Freiburg. Bearing frame
reinforced concrete. Walls clad with split tiles (Buchtal). Infill
panels clad with blue ceramic mosaic (10 x 10 cm.). Continuous
prefabricated concrete sun shades. Panels on the two storey workshop block clad with yellow split tiles. Experimental block (on the
right of the illustration): long façades of profiled aluminium sheet.
⋀ University Building Authorities I, Freiburg

Max Planck Institute of Nuclear Physics in Mainz. Reinforced
concrete frame, front faces of the exposed concrete floor slabs and
the rendered infill panels painted with a rubber-base paint (Amphibolin). End walls in facing brick. ⋀ Hans Joachim Lenz

294

295

295 Industrial research centre in Torrance/California. Expo
steel frame painted white. Infill walls and canopies of enar
ed steel sheet.   Å Risley, Gould and van Heu
296 Research Institute in St Germain/France. Blank wall surf
rendered and painted with a rubber-base paint (Indurin). Faç
panels of prefabricated reinforced concrete elements clad
small ceramic mosaic (2 x 2 cm.). Ground floor of the lo
block of rough stone.   Å Raymond Lo
297 Johann Reuchlin Museum of Decoration and Home Inte
in Pforzheim. Building for temporary exhibitions on the
steel frame construction. Decoration building (centre): alumi
curtain wall with alternate panels of frosted glass and
castings (Caspar KG Nöttingen), together with clear glass. H
museum (right): blank walls clad with rough Black Forest s
stone.   Å Manfred Lehmb

296

298

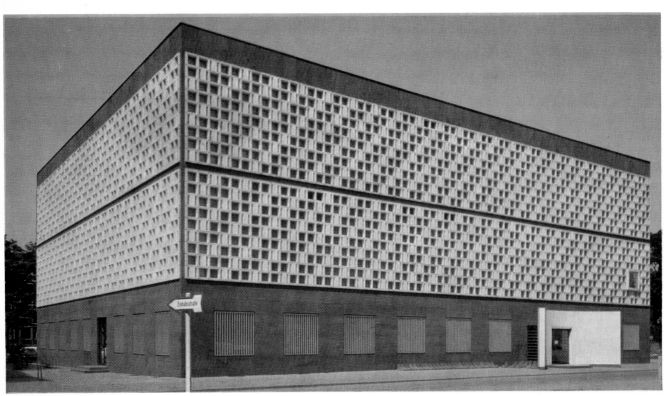

299

300

298 Local museum in The Hague. External walls in Gauinger travertine, partly in decorative relief bricks.　　　Ⱥ Main Building Authorities, The Hague

299 Kestner Museum in Hannover. The annexe, on a square grid, with the old museum as the core. Light walls of the upper floors with hanging honeycomb concrete, manufactured with white cement (Dyckerhoff). Ground-floor walls clad natural stone.　　　Ⱥ Werner Dierschke

300 Art Gallery in Hamburg. Bearing frame in reinforced concrete. Blank walls clad with brick. Gutters and front faces of the exposed concrete floor-beams covered with artificial stone slabs. Window wall frames and linking corridor in aluminium construction (Gartner) naturally anodised silicon grey　　　Ⱥ Building Authorities of Hamburg

301—302 Buildings in the 1965 international traffic exhibition in Munich. ⋏ Prof. Paolo Nestler
301 Railway service building on open terrain. Office block in prefabricated timber construction. Steel frame for the roof montage of broad flange beams, glosspainted an anthracite colour. Roof elements in a light timber construction, painted, like the walls, with a rubber-base paint (Diwagolan).
302 A children's traffic playground with pavilions and miniature practice roads. The buildings were a temporary erection and take the form of truncated cylinders, which vary in height, diameter and angle. Concrete ring foundations, superstructure in timber panels clad with asbestos cement slabs (Eternit). External walls of enamelled asbestos cement slabs (Eternit-Glasal) stuck one upon the other. The colours are related to the function of the pavilion: road-safety school = white, theatre = black, shops = red, aeroplane ride = blue, Post Office = yellow.

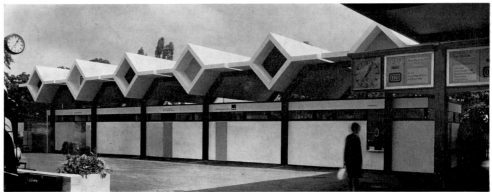

303

304

305

Buildings from the 1964 Swiss National Exhibition in Lausanne. Chief architect: Alberto Camenzini.

303 Good-value products sector. Open hall of twenty four funnel-shaped single elements, each of 18 x 18 m. span. Translucent skin of glass fibre reinforced synthetic material (Polyester) between light steel stiffeners. Columns of conical steel piping. Boundary walls in colour impregnated vertical timber. Ⓐ Florian Vischer and H. Hossdorf

304 The zone called 'The Port'. The group of tents around the small harbour gives the effect of a forest of sails. Their individual colours form powerful contrasts. Each tent has a surface area of 25 x 25 m. and is anchored at three points with steel cables which are tensioned to the concrete foundations with steel masts 13 m. high — these are partly sunk into the ground and partly into the bottom of the lake. Ⓐ Marc J. Saugey

305 The section called the 'Swiss Way'. Bearing construction composed of a system of parallel girders, arranged on a 1.20 m. spacing; these girders make up the side panels of the prisms. Continuous strip foundations of reinforced concrete. Translucent skin of plastic gives an optical contrast to the wooden beams of the gable Ⓐ Expo Architects Group

306 Sector 'Live Happily and Sensibly'. The landscaping and architectural massing correspond logically to the diversity of themes on display. Foundations in exposed concrete. Superstructure partly in steel, partly in timber. The buildings are entirely clad in timber (vertically and diagonally) and colour impregnated various tones.

Ⓐ Tita Carloni with Dr E. Staudacher and R. Siegenthaler

306

307

307 A hall at the Cologne Exhibition Centre. Building is entirely of aluminium (United Light Metal Works). Doors are colour anodised.
∧ Building Authorities of Cologne

308 Pavilion at the Hanover Fair. Structural steelwork. Cladding of the main building and gutter coverings of the entrance block of hot dip galvanised sheets, painted. Entrances in mahogany, clear-glossed. ∧ Friedrich Hüper

309 Exhibition hall at the Düsseldorf exhibition centre. Anodised aluminium exterior wall on a reinforced concrete skeleton. Enamelled aluminium panels (Gartner). Parapets on the external stairs painted with a rubber base paint.
∧ Building Authorities, Düsseldorf

310 Exhibition building for water-sport events in Palos Verde/California. Steel frame construction; bearing elements blue, panels red; ramps, parapets and water tanks glossed white.
∧ Pereira and Luckmann

311 Exhibition building at the Hanover Fair. The structural steel construction is strongly accentuated through the alternating paint tones. In a gap between the gutter coverings and the front faces of the exposed concrete floor slabs Venetian blinds are positioned.
∧ Richter and Wilke

308

312 Municipal exhibition centre in Offenburg. Reinforced concrete skeleton painted with a rubber-base paint. External wall of prefabricated relief concrete elements. The plinth is clad in split tiles. Gutters covered with enamelled steel sheets.
∧ Prof. A. Abele and Manfred Wacker

309

309a

310

311

312

312a

313

313 Exhibition hall at the Genoa exhibition centre. Bearing construction: reinforced concrete skeleton. The curtain wall elements are 3.50 m. high and consists of black, anodised aluminium profile frames, with asbestos cement panels (Eternit). The concrete peripheral beam of the all-round balcony on the intermediate floor is painted the colour of the asbestos cement panels. The recessed walls of the conference hall and of the surrounding buildings are a contrasting red.　　　　　　　　　　　　　　　　　　　　　　　　Å Maurizio Vitale

314

314 Section from an exhibition hall in Frankfurt/Main-Hoechst. External wall slabs coated with two layers of PVC (Hostalit). Panels of the recessed ground-floor walls of glass bricks.　Å Köhler

315 Mastersingers Hall in Nuremberg. Walls of the lower entrance building clad with Roman travertine or Norwegian quartzite. The exposed concrete slats on the glazed walls are painted with a dark grey rubber-base paint. The main building is clad with profiled aluminium.

Å Harald Loebermann

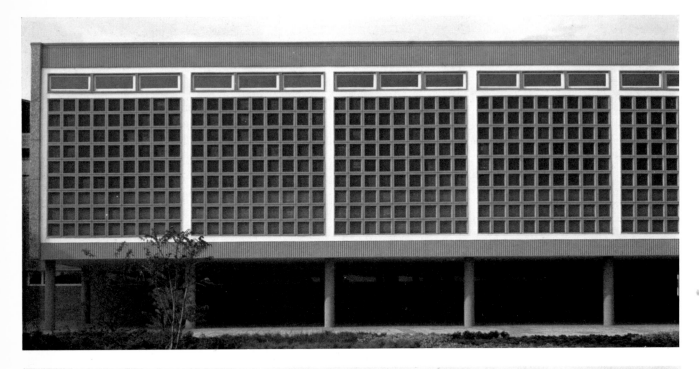

316 Main building and annexe of the municipal concert hall in Wolfsburg. Main building (colour illustration): external walls of the hall clad with smooth and profiled precast face textured concrete slabs (with a gravel surface), whose manufacture incorporates white cement (Dyckerhoff). Infill panels of coloured glass. Annexe (black-and-white illustration): the exposed faces of the reinforced concrete skeleton are painted white. Panelled window walls of concrete honeycomb painted grey. Gutters and front faces of the exposed concrete floor slabs covered with profiled steel sheets likewise painted grey.

Å Building Authorities, Wolfsburg

317 Cultural centre in Wolfsburg. Reinforced concrete construction. The staggered walls of the body of the building are clad with white and grey Carrara marble. These alternating colours create a strong horizontal effect which however is broken up by the vertical bands of windows which by day appear dark. The blank walls and underwindow panels in the recessed plinth are clad with black split tiles.

Å Prof. Alvar Aalto

317

318

319

20

318 Municipal Theatre in Krefeld. External wall elements of the window façades in bronze and copper sheeting (Wahlfeld). Blank façades in exposed masonry of glazed Dutch handpainted bricks. Panelled light giving walls near the entrance of glazed ceramic elements.   Å Prof. Gerhard Graubner
319 National theatre in Mannheim. The panelling of the reinforced concrete skeleton is travertine. The fly tower is of profiled copper sheet.   Å Prof. Gerhard Weber

320 The small auditorium of the Württemberg State Theatre in Stuttgart. Concrete roof band in patterned boarding. Wall facings of crystalline marble. Aluminium windows. Ground-floor masonry of Tranasgranit split slabs deeply jointed. Fly tower covered in copper sheeting.
    Å Hans Volkart, Kurt Pläcking, Bert Perlia
321 Detail from the entrance side of the concert hall in Stuttgart. Wall surface clad with coloured hard-burnt bricks. Concrete sculpture fixed on brackets.   Å Prof. Rolf Gutbrod and Prof. Adolf Abel

322 Municipal auditorium in Bergheim/Erft. Glass walls of the foyer in aluminium frames, anodised. The concrete bands of the floor slabs and gutters are clad with light metal. The windowless auditorium is clad entirely with unglazed yellow and white small split tiles, attractively arranged.   Å Jodokus Kehrer and Josef Heinrichs

322

323a

323

323b

323 Radio Televisione Italia centre in Naples. The individual parts of the building are characterised by their very different requirements; they are linked by covered bridges, stairs and walkways. Illustration no. 323 shows the rear view of the radio and television studios with an emergency staircase which is accessible from each floor at two points. The external walls are clad entirely with small split tiles. Staircase is of metal painted two colours. In the foreground there is a connecting corridor with window walls. Concert-hall building (323 a and b): the bearing concrete walls are clad with marble. The high-level building is clad on the street side with relief ceramic slabs and on the end façades with ceramic strips. Stairs have light metal coverings and the balustrades are of safety glass. The doors are in beaten copper.

A Raffaele Contigiani and Renato de Martino

324 Protestant church in Rheinhausen. External walls entirely clad with ceramic slabs of various formats and tonings. Doors in copper.   Å Esch

325 Theatre in a park in Grenchen/Switzerland. Bearing walls clad with brick. Roofs and super-structures clad in copper.
                 Å Ernst Gisel with Giovanni Crivelli

324

325

326

nastery church in Meschede. The
complex is in facing brick accen-
by the horizontally and vertically
d bands of windows.

ʎ Hans Schilling
testant church of the Holy Ghost
sburg. Walls partly in exposed
e, partly in rendered brick paint-
h a rubber-base paint (Indurin).
vered in copper.

ʎ Prof. Alvar Aalto

327

328

329

330

331

328 The Church of Catherine St Birgitta in Lübeck. Reinforced concrete roof on twelve cross-shaped supports. Walls in reinforced hollow bricks (visible internally) and clad externally with ceramic slabs (Buchtal). Louvres on the tower in exposed concrete. ⋏ Georg and Hermann Lippsmeier

329 Protestant church of St Matthew in Erzingen. The concrete panels of the tower are white and painted medium grey with a rubber-base paint. The church itself is clad with light grey granulated asbestos cement façade slabs (Eternit-Colorit).
⋏ Stephan Müller

330 Catholic church in Lauenstein. Gable walls and border walls rendered and painted terracotta colour. Gutters covered in zinc sheet painted a contrasting white. Masonry of the longitudinal façades and of the projecting entrance block of white chalk sandstone, with light-coloured joints. Roof covering of slate slabs. Entrance door of black, gloss-painted timber with white-enamelled handles.
⋏ Ernst-Otto Rossbach and Hans H. Priesemann

331 Detail of the courtyard side of the Paul-Gerhard church in Mannheim. Swedish quartzite and coloured glass mosaic (Design: Prof. Blasius Spreng). Door in beaten copper. Adjacent wall of specially formed concrete elements.
⋏ Gerhard Schlege

333

334

335

338a

332 (Page 173) Model joiner's workshop in Mülheim/Ruhr. Gutters in exposed concrete, painted. Masonry walls clad with 24.5 x 12 cm. split tiles (Gail). The intermediate areas under and over the windows are rendered and painted with a rubber-base paint. 	Ⓐ Prof. Walter Henn

333 Industrial building in Pomezia/Italy. Bearing skeleton in reinforced concrete; faces of frame painted grey. Panelling of large facing bricks. 	Ⓐ Enrico Lente

334 Furniture factory in Bovisio/Italy. Reinforced concrete skeleton. Ground floor clad with natural stone slabs. Upper floors of the exhibition hall clad with painted, profiled steel sheets. Administrative building clad with small, white, ceramic mosaic; infill panels of coloured glass.
	Ⓐ Antonio Giosué and Umberto Turri

335 Laboratory for Aero and Hydrodynamics of the Polytechnic in Delft/Holland. Exposed parts of the reinforced concrete frame painted. Projecting cladding of chalk sandstone. Doors red, other metal parts glossed an anthracite colour.
	Ⓐ Van den Broek and Bakema

336 Factory producing synthetic materials in Yverdon/Switzerland. Exposed concrete structure and rendered infill panels painted with a rubber-base paint. Timber clear-varnished. 	Ⓐ Ed. Schachtner

337 Textile factory with administrative building near Bregenz/Austria. Exposed concrete structure and facing masonry painted with mineral paints (Keim). Window frames glossed black, casements white. 	Ⓐ Franz Seitz

338 Punched-card printing works in Böblingen. Cantilevered flat roof constructed in steel. Walls of 5 x 1 m. gas concrete slabs, painted.
	Ⓐ Kieferle and Rödl

336

337

338

339

340

339 Saw tooth roofed shed of an industrial works in Brunswick. Bearing construction in reinforced concrete. Cladding of flame-coloured narrow split tiles. Ŋ Prof. Walter Henn

340 Manufacturing shed of a works in Dörningheim/Hanau. Shell frames of reinforced concrete, painted dark grey. Panelling of the side walls of 12.5 cm. thick Siporex slabs. Joints are a contrasting red. Ŋ Prof. Walter Henn

341 Hangars of a camera works in Munich. Side walls clad with narrow, split tiles in a mixed heather colour. Ŋ K. A. Koppenhöfer

342 Repairs work shop of the Zürich post office. Bearing construction in reinforced concrete. Roof superstructures rendered and painted with a rubber-base paint. A concrete ring is continued over the side walls and accentuated by the colour of its paint. Side walls clad in brick deep jointed Window walls of steel framework glossed grey. Ŋ Farner and Grunder

341

342

343 Section from the façade of a works in Hagen. Reinforced concrete skeleton filled with gas concrete slabs. The colours of the paint (dark grey/white) underline the structural joints. Steel windows glossed red.

 Å Prof. Walter Henn

344 Textile factory in Tailfingen/Württemberg. Plinth rendered and painted. The flat cube block is clad with precast face textured concrete slabs. Side walls of the block in the background are clad vertically with timber.

Å Werner Luz

343

344

345

345 Factory in Heidelberg-Leimen. External walls clad with asbestos cement slabs (Eternit). Roof superstructure of painted corrugated sheet. Metal doors glossed red.   Ⱥ Prof. Ernst Neufert

346 Machines factory in Munich. High block (above): reinforced concrete skeleton accentuated by grey paint. Infill panels in exposed concrete, painted white. Low block (below): steel construction. Curtain wall of anodised light metal, with infill panels of enamelled steel sheet.   Ⱥ Prof. Walter Henn

347 Manufacturing shop in Homburg/Saar. Steel frame, steel window frames and steel-sheet doors painted blue gloss (Gartner). Walls of facing engineering bricks.   Ⱥ Building Department of the INA Needle Bearing Works

348 Assembly shop of a steel firm in Gundelfingen/ Danube. Steel frame with similarly steelframed window walls and enamelled panels (Gartner). Wall panels in facing engineering bricks.

349 Works in Wesel. Reinforced concrete construction, painted dark grey. Windows of coloured compound glass. The wall panels of the lower block are clad with narrow split tiles. Rendered areas of the linking block painted with a rubber base paint.   Ⱥ Prof. Walter Henn

350 Machines works in Aerzen near Hamlin. Steel frame painted black. Facing brickwork. Window bands of Profilit glazing; opening casements a contrasting white. Continuous sun shades of light metal. Steel-sheet doors glossed (Ducolux).   Ⱥ Prof. Walter Henn

346

347

348

349

350

351

351 Bottling plant of a brewery in Passau. Rendered structural walls painted with a rubber-base paint. Colours: plinth dark grey, horizontal divisioning white, areas between the windows brown, recessed spandrels between the narrow window openings, light grey (colour scheme by Willy Torsten).   Å H. E. Wörlen
352 Printing works in Wuppertal-Elberfeld. Steel construction, electrically welded, with horizontal sun blinds (Gartner). Blank areas on the window walls as well as the dividing concrete lamellas of the front stair well painted white. Front façades of the stair wells clad with ceramic elements.   Å Willy Hornung

352

353

353 Laboratories of the State Military Testing Centre in Zürich-Dübendorf. Reinforced concrete skeleton; vertical faces light grey, front faces of the continuous concrete floors painted white. Panels of brick cladding. Windows of light metal, black frames. Roof covering of asbestos cement (Eternit). Front edge of the roof projection in a contrasting blue.

Å Werner Forrer

354 Industrial building of a pharmaceutical factory in Mannheim-Waldhof. Reinforced concrete skeleton (*in situ* and prefabricated parts combined), painted with a rubber-base paint. Areas over the windows clad with colour-treated asbestos cement corrugated sheets (Eternit). Door and spandrels of the emergency staircase gloss-painted.

Å Prof. Heinrich Schmitt, Gerd V. Heene, Werner Böninger, Peter Biedermann

354

355

355 Steelworks in Beeckerwerth. The entire industrial plant is of Thyssendach (Profil 70/250) and composite panel insulated Thyssenwand (Profil 41/375). The surfaces are partly clad with PVC and partly painted. The individual works are of contrasting colours which on the one hand underline the divisioning of the plant and yet on the other bring the extensive complex down to manageable proportions for the people working there. The total effect of the plant in its landscape and its massing is one of discrimination, enhancing the appearance. Colour design: Studio for colour advice: Å Architect: Building Department of the August-Thyssen-Hütte A. G.

356

356 Storehouse for a purchasing cooperative in Biel/Switzerland. Reinforced concrete skeleton, painted. Infill panels and windows in light metal. Panelling masonry in the recessed part of the plinth rendered and painted with a rubber-base paint.   Å Gianpeter Gaudy

357 Store of a rubber-factory in Munich. Supports in exposed concrete, painted grey. Panelling and infill panels clad with matt glazed, ceramic tiles (19.5 x 9.5 cm.). Windows in Afzelia, untreated. Folded roof and doors of aluminium sheet.   Å Prof. Franz Hart

357

358

358 Storehouse of a large ironmongery factor in Dietikon near Zürich. Through the colour contrast between the blank, painted, rendered areas and the panelling of facing brick there results, together with the light contrasting reinforced concrete skeleton, a strong emphasis on structure which corresponds to the functional divisioning of the complex.

359

359 Bus station on the island of Kyushu/Japan. Infill panels of dark blue glazed tiles. Undersides of the cantilevering main building clad with aluminium slabs. Canopies over the bus stops white and blue.   Ⱥ Masachika Murata

360 Retail office and goods store of an industrial works in Los Angeles/California. Walls of formed concrete slabs, painted. Canopy construction: steel profile frames with suspended soffite in timber. Lettering also of timber. White sun roller blinds.   Ⱥ Pereira and Luckmann

360

361

361 Travel agency in the USA. Continuous cladding of anodised aluminium with superimposed internally lit lettering. Beneath this there is a sun shade of enamelled steel framework with light expanded metal infill. Tower and blank walls on the ground floor rendered and painted contrasting colours.

362 Section from an office block of a car repair works in Leonberg. Bearing skeleton in reinforced concrete painted with a rubber-base paint. Infill panels of brick. Window frames black. Glass beads a contrasting white.   Ⱥ Ostertag

3 Office and store of the Milan service
ation on the Milan-Serravalle autostrada.
ffice block in steel construction. Supports
d front faces of the continuous concrete
or slabs painted white. Rear, blank walls
ed with unglazed ceramic tiles. Windows
d infill panels of the roof floor of colour
odised aluminium. On the recessed en-
nce-floor there is a strong colour fresco.
 reinforced concrete canopy 64 m. long
tends over a series of toll booths which
e prefabricated of sheet steel.

ᴧ Carlo Casati

4 Milan-Serravalle autostrada check and
st point. Building and its canopy of rein-
rced concrete, entirely clad with small
ramic mosaic. Windows and doors in alu-
nium. ᴧ Carlo Casati

363

364

365

366

365 Fire station in Cedar Rapids, Iowa/USA. Light me
frame construction. Wall elements of asbestos ceme
coated externally with coloured glass-fibre materi
Inserted cladding walls of facing brick.
                                    Å Crites and McConn
366 Telecommunications centre in Peine. Bearing ste
frame painted black. Compound elements of timb
framework with aluminium external walls. Windo
likewise of aluminium. Blank end walls of facing bri
                                              Å OPD, Hanov

367

368

367 Water works in Los Angeles/California. The blank wall is painted and protected with an aluminium cooling shield.　　Ⱥ William L. Pereira and Associates
368 District heating plant in Mödling/Austria. Reinforced concrete skeleton and blank areas rendered and painted with a white rubber-base paint. Plinth clad with red, unglazed split tiles (Buchtal) and the window infills clad with the same material in a leather colour. Doors and windows glossed dark green.
　　Ⱥ Matthäus Siszda

369

369 Power station in Hanover. External wall of the towers of light metal framework with blue-grey Polycolor glass; the projecting large panels in facing brick. Turbine rooms: bearing walls partly in facing brick, partly clad with white ceramic slabs (Gail) with dark joints.
Ⱥ Rudolf Christfreund and the Building Authorities of Hanover

369a

371

370 (Page 191) Car agency in Agno/Switzerland. Bearing skeleton of prefabricated reinforced concrete elements. Blank areas clad with brick. Ʌ Bruno Brocchi

372

371 Office and shop block in Brunswick. Curtain wall with steel tube ribs (internally) and light metal profiles (externally). Infill elements of insulated slabs with light grey Polycolor mirror glass in front.
Ʌ Prof. Dr F. W. Kraemer
372 A chemist's shop in Langenhagen bei Hannover. Shop clad with ceramic mosaic. Walls of the flats clad with split tiles. Continuous separating concrete gutters and timber balcony balustrades painted white.
Ʌ H. A. Kleinschmid

373 Block of shops in Munich. Bearing skeleton in reinforced concrete. Curtain wall of steel and aluminium with compound infill panels. Upper shop area boarded vertically with red wood.
Ʌ Prof. Rolf Gutbier, Hans Kammerer and Walter Belz
374 Shopping centre in Wolfsburg. Steel frame. Flat roof gutter facing and edge of terrace clad with enamelled asbestos cement slabs (Eternit). Walls clad with split tiles (Gail). Timber of the windows painted dark grey. Lettering fascia a contrasting red.
Ʌ Pof. Paul Baumgarten

373

374

375

377a

376

377

375 Department store in Hamburg. Reinforced concrete skeleton. Upper floor clad with ceramic tiles: special L-shaped units on corners. Plinth, ramp and gutter facing of the porter's lodge clad in two colours of medium sized (5 x 5 cm.) ceramic mosaic. Office block in facing brick. Gutters and front faces of the continuous concrete floor slabs are a light contrasting colour. ʎ Schramm and Elingius

376 Block of shops in Berlin-Friedenau. Reinforced concrete frame. External walls of compound slabs with an outer layer of enamelled light grey steel. Steel windows glossed dark blue. Raked sunshades of white-enamelled steel sheet. Display windows entirely of glass, equiped with electrically-operated sun blinds.
ʎ Hans Schaefers

377 Department store in Berlin-Steglitz. Upper floor of the selling area clad with profiled ceramic elements and dark jointed. Walls of the stair well clad with small ceramic mosaic (4 x 4 cm.). The unbroken areas of the plinth area clad with narrow split tiles. Windows painted white. ʎ Otto Sperber

378

378 Department Store in Heerbrugg/Switzerland. Reinforced concrete skeleton, external exposed parts painted dark grey. Walls clad in panels of shiny asbestos cement in various sizes and two colours (Eternit). The blue sun-shades form a contrast. ʎ Hanspeter Nüesch

379 Block of shops in Duisburg. The whole building is clad with polished Swedish granite. Window bands of anodised aluminium. The uniting sun blinds are in yellow.
ʎ Wilhelm Cloes

379

381a

380

381

380 An indoor market in Rome. Reinforced concrete construction, painted. Panels of red scratched render. Plinth and stairs clad with natural stone slabs. ⋏ Ufficio Technico dell' Annona Comune di Roma
381 Self-service grocery store in Rome. Steel frame covered with galvanised, dark grey glossed sheet. Cladding of travertine slabs. Windows and doors of aluminium. ⋏ Prof. Giuseppe Perugini

382

383

382 Department store in Hamburg-Harburg. External surfaces of structure in exposed concrete, spray painted. Continuous band on the first floor clad with relief ceramic tiles (Gail). Main block clad with anthracite-coloured ceramic tiles, car park clad with white, glazed, ceramic tiles. Ⓐ Walter Brune

383 Furniture shop in Heerlen/Holland. External walls of timber frame clad with grey-glossed aluminium profiled sheets. Front faces of the neonlight boxes red, continuous cladding over the display windows glossed dark blue. Ⓐ R. E. M. Wolfs

384

386a

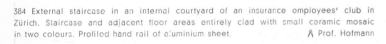

384 External staircase in an internal courtyard of an insurance employees' club in Zürich. Staircase and adjacent floor areas entirely clad with small ceramic mosaic in two colours. Profiled hand rail of aluminium sheet. Å Prof. Hofmann

385

Refectory of the Brunswick Technical High School. Steel frame. Blank wall areas clad with natural stone (Cebrato). Window walls of timber/aluminium. Continuous gutter facing galvanised trapezium sheet, painted.

⋏ Prof. Walter Henn

Restaurant in Westfalen Park in Dortmund. Painted steel frame. The timber panel frames and slatted roller blinds, and also the external wall cladding, of colour-impregnated timber. ⋯mney and boundary walls of chalk sandstone. Hand rail of white glossed square profiles with timber boards below.

⋏ Groth, Schlote and Lehmann

387

387 Cafeteria of a car works in Stuttgart. Structural walls, rendered and painted with a rubber-base paint. Windows and canopy a contrasting colour.   Ⲁ Building Department of Daimler-Benz Ltd.
388 The canteen kitchen of a steel works in Duisburg. Structure of the upper floor painted light grey. Ground-floor cladding of narrow split tiles. Steel windows have infill panels of dark grey glass.   Ⲁ Lutz Voigtländer
389 Town Hall in Nordwalde. Reinforced concrete skeleton painted externally with a rubber-base paint (Diwagolan). Brick cladding in panels. Timber windows painted with white gloss. Slate roof.   Ⲁ Prof. Harald Deilmann

388

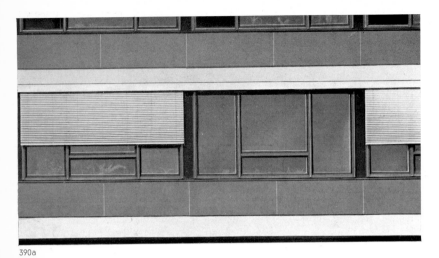

390a

391a

390 District Council Offices in Leonberg. Gable and walls clad with glass mosaic. Spandrel bands of enamelled steel sheet. Windows painted in the same grey colour. Light metal sun blinds. Unbroken walls of the conference hall clad with granite slabs. Copper gutters. Ⱥ Haigis and Welz

391 Town Hall in Korntal. Reinforced concrete structure from which continuous strips of natural stone slabs (quartzite) are hung. Timber windows; fixed panes painted black, casements white. End façades of exposed concrete painted with a rubber-base paint. Ⱥ K. H. Neumann and Hans Breg

390

391

392

392 Town Hall in Peine. Bearing skeleton in reinforced concrete. Gutter facings, floor slabs and plinth clad with white Lasa marble. Walls clad with Dutch hand-painted bricks. Spandrels of coloured glass. Recessed part of the plinth painted black.　　　　 Å Martin and Inge Düker
393 View of the inner courtyard of the District Council Offices in Tecklenburg/Westphalia. Aluminium curtain wall with timber/aluminium windows and infill panels of coloured glass.　　　　 Å Wolfgang and Ruth Pantenius

393

394 Detail from the Law Courts in Lübeck. Bearing steel construction. Cladding of precast face textured concrete slabs, manufactured with black Norwegian Labrador stone. Recessed plinth clad with exposed aggregate concrete slabs. Timber windows have external aluminium cladding. Projecting steel facing members, zinc-sprayed and painted white.　　　　　　　　　　A Atmer and Marlow

395

394

396

395 Cantonal Police Station in Lucerne. Supports, infill panels and end façades in concrete — partly *in situ* and partly prefabricated. The rubber-base paint in two colours underlines the architectural structure of the building.
　　　　　　　　　　　　　　　　　　　　　　A Werner and Max Ribary

396 Post Office and flats in Zürich. Windows and gutter coverings of the two-storey block and the security grille on the ground floor of aluminium. Continuous band above the counter area rendered and painted. Flats clad with enamelled steel sheet.
　　　　　　　　　　　　　　　　　　　　　　A Rob. Bachmann

397

397 Police Facilities Building in Santa Ana/California. Unbroken end façades clad with 120 x 240 cm. slabs of treated, exposed aggregate concrete. Plinth on the entrance side rendered and painted white. Sunshade louvres in front of the window wall of vertical, hard enamelled steel elements. Canopy in aluminium.   Å Richard J. Neutra
398 District Council Offices in Münster/Westphalia. All external walls clad with red granite slabs. Windows and window walls in aluminium. Exposed concrete canopy.
Å Prof. Harald Deilmann

398

399

399a

399 Welfare offices in Essen. Bearing
reinforced concrete frame. Underwindow panels clad with 5 x 24.5 cm.
glazed split tiles (Buchtal) jointed
with light coloured cement. Window
walls of steel framework gloss painted a charcoal colour. The windows
and external wall compound frames
are so arranged that they correspond
to the required room divisions and
consequently the very strict external
wall divisioning has an attractive
appearance. Plinth and end façades
rendered and painted with a rubber-
base paint the colour of the steel
framework.   Å P. F. Schneider

400 Italian Institute for External Trade in Rome. Skeleton of reinforced concrete. External walls of steel construction. Steel profile columns on a 1.70 m. module with regular window and infill units of light metal. External Venetian blinds are likewise of light metal. Fountain of natural stone with a bronze dish in the centre distributing the water. Ⓐ Antonio Antonelli and Manfredo Greco

401 The Finance Ministry of Hesse in Wiesbaden. Walls panelled in glass mosaic. Exposed front faces of the continuous concrete floor slabs acting as dividers are painted. The sun blinds are all yellow whilst the window frames are white-painted. Staircase wall of prefabricated concrete fretwork with roughcast glass. Canopy on steel supports, underside clad with timber.
△ Hans Köhler and Rolf Himmelreich

401

401a

401b

2 Section from a façade of the Lower Saxony Land Parliament in Hanover. Granite slabs (125 x 220 cm.) hung with open joints in front of the concrete walls. Steel windows glossed
rk grey. Plinth clad with sandstone.   Å Prof. Dieter Oesterlen
3 Land Parliament Building of Baden-Württemberg in Stuttgart. Curtain walls of bronze (Gartner) on the reinforced concrete structure, heat absorbing coloured glass; Venetian blinds
anged between glass panes.   Å Prof. Linde, Heinle, Kiessling, Schmidtberger, Winkler

404a

404 Ministry of Finance in Rome. Steel external wall hung on the bearing reinforced concrete construction, with enamelled infill panels.
⅄ Vittorio Cafiero, Cesare Ligini, Guido Marinucci, Renato Venturi

404

405 A landscape architect's office in Ludwigshafen. Timber frame. Panelling of blank walls in facing semi-engineering bricks. Window elements painted white with infill panels of asbestos cement (Eternit) Doors glossed. Pergola of timber construction.
⅄ Prof. Heinrich Schmitt and Gerd Heene

406

406 Administrative block of the University Hospital in Freiburg. Exposed concrete skeleton and asbestos cement slab cladding painted with a rubber-base paint (Protopon). Recessed plinth clad with vertical timber boarding.
⋏ University Building Authorities, Freiburg
407 Branch bank in Milan. Light metal curtain wall, anodised a graphite colour. Windows and panels in natural anodised aluminium. Blank walls partly clad with facing brick. All the sun blinds are blue.
⋏ Renzo Zavanella
408 Section from an administrative building in Rome. Skeleton of prefabricated concrete elements. Window wall glossed partly white and partly black. Infill panels of green glass.

409 Branch of a bank in Munich. Folded roof supported on seamless steel tubes clad with non-warping timber panelling. Copper sheet roof. Cross-shape supports in exposed concrete. Core of the building in naturally anodised aluminium. Blank end walls clad in Italian conglomerate stone.
⋏ Prof. Fred Angerer

407

408

410

410 Administration block of a mens' clothing factory in Offenburg/Baden. Reinforced concrete skeleton rendered and painted with a plastic paint. External skin of the sandwich slabs of enamelled steel sheet. White-glossed timber windows.   Å Müller, Wacker and Stephan

411

412

413

411 Administration block of a distributing firm in Cologne-Frechen. Reinforced concrete frame clad with white enamelled steel sheet elements, infill panels of the same material, but blue (Salm). Light metal sun blinds.
Ⱥ Reinhold Weber

412 Administration block in Düsseldorf. Brick walls clad with yellow, glazed facing bricks. Front faces of the exposed concrete floor slab clad with white marble. Windows and doors in steel, painted a graphite grey.
Ⱥ Prof. Godber Nissen

413 Bank in Viersen. Steel bearing construction painted grey-black. Window wall units are anodised aluminium with aluminium panels (Gartner).
Ⱥ Hans Schleich

414

414a

414 The administration block of a refinery in Cologne. Steel curtain wall over a reinforced concrete structure, with infill panels of enamelled steel sheet (Salm). Plinth rendered and painted. Ancillary block (see illustration 414 a) has a steel construction and a folded roof. Walls clad with yellow narrow split tiles.   A A. E. Palme

415

416

15 Administration block in Rome. Rear main block of untreated exposed concrete. Infill elements and façade of the building in the foreground of enamelled aluminium.   ⋏ Luigi Piccinato
16 First-aid centre for a works in Düsseldorf. Wall and window elements are of aluminium on a steel frame. Prefabricated concrete main structure. Continuous infill panels and external ght metal Venetian blinds.   ⋏ The Architectural Office of Henkel and Co. GmbH.

417 Administration block of the GEMA in Berlin. Precast face textured concrete slabs form the external cladding, together with black, white and predominantly red marble additives. Windows painted white, blind boxes yellow. Flower trough in front of the plinth in black precast face textured concrete.
Å Prof. Rudolf Büchner and Klaus Zimmermann
418 Main administration block of a works in Nordhorn. Reinforced concrete frame. Exposed concrete areas painted in two colours of a rubber-base paint (Basis Propiofan). Continuous, uniform sunshade in an appropriate colour. Å Werner Zobel

417

418

419

419 Administration and exhibition building of a factory in Bologna. Bearing reinforced concrete frame; front faces of the exposed concrete floor slabs and gutters painted with a rubber-base paint. Blank wall areas and infill panels clad with facing brick. Columns between the windows clad with small ceramic mosaic. Light metal Venetian blinds. Supports of the exhibition block and the boundary walls clad with natural stone.   Å Dr Francesco Santini

420

420a

420 Administration block in Berlin. Aluminium curtain walls over a reinforced concrete structure, with infill panels of smoothened marble (Verde Frayé on the low block and Lasa marble on the upper floors). Illustration 420 a shows the main entrance to the building.

Ⱥ Gerhard Krebs

421

421a

421 Insurance office in Milan. In parts red marble cladding; end bay and ground floor surfaces clad with light-coloured marble. Aluminium windows with light-coloured sun blinds. Railings on the vaults (on the right of illustration 421 a) of light metal.   Ѧ Studio Ponti, Fornaroli, Rosselli and Studio Portaluppi

422 Section from the main façade of a bank in Düsseldorf. External wall cladding of smoothened marble (Chipolino), windows glossed blue, glazing beads white. The yellow sun blinds form a contrast.   Ѧ Prof. Dr Hentrich and H. Petschnigg

423 Insurance building in Stuttgart. Reinforced concrete structure. Anodised aluminium curtain wall, with marble infill panels. Ѧ Prof. Rolf Gutbier, Hans Kammerer and Walter Belz

422

423

424

425

426

427

428

429

424 Section from an insurance building in Brunswick. Continuous reinforced concrete bands clad with black precast face textured concrete. Timber windows painted white.
Ⱥ Prof. Dr F. W. Kraemer

425 Section from the administration block of a machines factory in Munich. External curtain wall in a light metal construction with aluminium infill panels.
Ⱥ Prof. Walter Henn

426 Office block in Düsseldorf. Window bands in aluminium (Gartner), silicon grey, with naturally anodised casements. Infill panels of coloured precast face textured slabs.
Ⱥ Prof. Dr Hentrich and H. Petschnigg

427 Bank in Berlin. Reinforced concrete skeleton. Under window bands clad with white marble, ground-floor walls clad with greenish marble. Blank areas under clearstoreys clad with small ceramic mosaic.
Ⱥ Helmut Ollk

428 Editorial office of a newspaper in Milan. Reinforced concrete frame painted light grey; rendered infill panels painted with a blue rubber-base paint. Windows and doors in aluminium.
Ⱥ Giorgio Morpurgo, Mario Silvani, Virgilio Vercelloni

429 Administration block in Frankfurt/Main. Spandrels clad with aluminium panels (Gartner). Surface naturally silken-matt anodised with an impressed red band.
Ⱥ Prof. Alfred H. Caspari

430 Administration block in Dornbirn/Austria. Exposed concrete surfaces painted with mineral paint (Keim). Narrow strips between the aluminium windows clad with enamelled asbestos cement elements (Eternit-Glasal).
Ⱥ Franz Seitz

430

431

432

433

431 Section from the façade of the administration block of a works in Düsseldorf-Reisholz. Spandrel bands clad with variably coloured ceramic tiles. Windows in light metal. Between the windows and the spandrel claddings narrow strips of exposed facing concrete have been retained.

∦ W. Heinicke

432 Office block of an insurance firm in Heilbronn. Spandrel bands clad with coloured glass mosaic. Windows painted white. Blank end walls in exposed concrete.

∦ Traub and Heer

433 Bank in Bonn. Continuous spandrels clad with glazed, profiled split tiles (Buchtal). Window frames clear varnished, casements glossed white. Uniform, striped sunblinds.

∦ Schmidt, van Dorp, Kron, Hitz

434

434 Industrial administration building in Milan. External walls clad with unglazed 12 x 24.5 cm. white and grey split tiles (Buchtal) Aluminium window walls.

∦ Gian Luigi Giordani and Ippolito Malaguzzi

435 Administration block of a works in La Ferté-Gaucher/France. Solid infill panels clad with ceramic mosaic in various colours. Window walls and canopy in steel painted dark colour.

∦ Architectural office Villeroy and Boch

435

436

437

Electro-technic shop in Frankfurt/Main. The complex consists of three buildings of ⎡rent heights. On the main building the spandrel bands are clad with rhomboid-⎡ed, profiled aluminium elements. Linking blocks are one and two storeys and are ⎡ with ceramic mosaic in two colours. Light metal windows. See also illustration ⎡86. Ⱥ Otto Apel
⎡Administration block of a ladies' wear factory in Milan. External walls are entirely ⎡ with glazed split tiles. Aluminium windows. The supports are similarly clad with ⎡inium. Ⱥ Dr Frederico Castiglioni

438

438 Administration block of an insurance company in Wiesbaden. Blank areas of the end façade clad with glazed split tiles. Faces of the exposed concrete floor slabs a contrasting light colour. Concrete parapets in front of the door to each floor painted blue. Infill panels of the longitudinal façade of steel frames with concrete slabs and cladding of glass mosaic, all prefabricated. Plinth clad with red split tiles. Pergola like construction on the roof is of light metal. Ⱥ Fr. Rettig

439

440

441

439 Administration block of a works in Biel/Switzerland. Steel frame. External skin of the compound infill elements of stoved, glossed steel sheet. Rendered staircase wall and windows painted white.
ꓘ Brechbühl and Itten

440 Constructional office of a steel building firm in Hanover. Steel construction, glossed graphite grey. Infill panels of grey mirror glass, steel window frames a contrasting white.   ꓘ Franz Richter and Heinz Wilke

441 Administration building in Rome. Exposed steel frame glossed red. Windows and infill elements of aluminium, naturally anodised. Exposed concrete parts a contrasting dark grey. Roof space protected from the sun by a light metal framework.   ꓘ Pediconi, Paniconi, Passarelli

442 Office block of an insurance company in Osnabrück. Pilotis in smoothened precast concrete slabs. External wall frames one storey high, with white-glossed timber casements; between the panes of glass there are sunshade blinds; infill panels of Polycolor glass. Front faces of the floor slabs clad with black-painted steel sheet. Vertical steel supports, unclad, project beyond the external wall.   ꓘ Prof. Dr F. W. Kraemer

443 Section from the administration block of an industrial concern in Zürich. Bearing frame of prefabricated concrete elements. Naturally anodised aluminium external wall. Infill panels of dark green glass. Plinth clad with marble slabs.   ꓘ Farner and Grunder

444 Section from an industrial building in Cologne-Deutz. Infill panels of prefabricated elements with glazed natural stone slabs cast into the concrete (Andesit).
ꓘ Building Department of Klöckner-Humboldt-Deutz AG

442

443

444

445

445 Corporation depot of the town of Solo-thurn/Switzerland. Reinforced concrete frame. Aluminium curtain wall with coloured glass infill panels. Panels on the ground floor rendered and painted with a rubber-base paint. Supports on the ground floor and retaining wall in exposed concrete.　Ⓐ Hans Luder

446 Administration block of a travel agency in Hanover. Aluminium curtain wall on a reinforced concrete frame with glass infill panels (Opal). Plinth rendered and painted.　Ⓐ Rolf Wekel

446

447

448

447 Printing works of a newspaper concern in Berlin. Curtain wall in timber/aluminium; infill panels of Poly-color glass. Gutter facing and plinth clad with ceramic tiles (Gail). Å Bega and Franzi, Sobotka and Müller

448 Bank in Basle. Aluminium curtain wall. Infill panels of hardened mirror glass with stoved, glossed, inner face. Supports clad with Grinatal. Å Suter and Suter

449

449 Administration block of an Einkaufsverband in Fürth. Window walls in steel frame with infill elements of enamelled steel sheet (Salm). Blank wall areas of facing brick. Boundary walls of light constructional bricks.   Ⱥ Alex Weber

450 Bank in Hamburg. Curtain wall in light metal construction with dark anodised areas (Nipp). Gutter facing to the first floor in untreated aluminium; on this level the infill panels are of horizontal oiled teak. Walls on the ground floor clad with natural stone (Diabas).   Ⱥ Klaus Martens
451 Rented office accommodation of an insurance company in Hanover. Aluminium curtain wall with dark brown stoved, glossed infill elements.   Ⱥ Prof. Dr F. W. Kraemer

450

451

452

452 Administration block of an iron foundry in Peine. Steel curtain wall on a reinforced concrete frame. Infill panels of enamelled steel sheet. Windows of anodised light metal. Steel mullions zinc sprayed and glossed (Ducolux). End walls in facing brick.　Å Prof. Dieter Oesterlen

453 Office and shop block in Munich. In front of the recessed window wall there is a sunshade of Carrara marble.   Å Prof. Paul Stohrer
454 Clearing house in Essen. External walls and projecting, continuous sunshades clad with enamelled sheet steel. Aluminium windows. Canopy in steel and aluminium; soffite and entrance walls clad with timber.
Å Prof. Heinrich Bartmann

455 Administration block of an insurance company in Pasadena/California. Reinforced concrete frame. Window walls shaded with a construction consisting of vertical aluminium bands and horizontal gold anodised aluminium bars.   Å Welton Becket and Associates
456 Administration block in Berlin. Reinforced concrete frame with a sunshade of swivel-mounted, vertical, standing asbestos cement (Eternit) in two colours.   Å Helmut Ollk

454

453

454a

455

456

457

458

459

460

457 Trades Union House in Saarbrücken. External walls clad with glazed ceramic medium-sized mosaic.   Å W. Nobis
458 Administration building of the Hanover transport undertaking. Reinforced concrete clad with precast face textured concrete slabs. Window elements and Venetian blind boxes of anodised light metal: fixed parts in a natural colour, opening parts anthracite colour. Window infills of coloured glass. Manager's balcony has an enamelled light metal sheet balustrade.   Å Prof. Dieter Oesterlen
459 Guards Barracks in Helsinki. Window wall has a timber frame, finished externally with porcelain enamel. Infill panels of coloured glass (Detopak). Blank end walls and plinth clad with natural stone slabs. The gutter facings and roof superstructure are of painted steel sheet.   Å Viljo Revell
460 Geico Building in Chevy Chase, Maryland/USA. Steel frame construction. Blank wall areas and infill panels clad with enamelled steel. Glazing with coloured crystal mirrorglass (United Glass Works, Aachen).   Å Vincent G. Kling
461 State Institute for Social Welfare in Rome. Exposed concrete frame. Cladding of marble slabs (Carrara). Aluminium window elements with narrow infills of coloured glass.   Å M. Paniconi, G. Pediconi, M. Raffo

461a

461

462

462 Administration building in Essen. External walls clad with lampblack, matt glazed split tiles (Buchtal). Light metal windows naturally anodised. Steel canopy painted.   ↟ Prof. Egon Eiermann and Robert Hilgers
463 Portion of the main façade of the Chamber of Industry and Commerce in Essen. External walls entirely clad with enamelled steel sheet. White painted windows.   ↟ Prof. Heinrich Bartmann
464 Section from the main façade of an administrative buliding in Essen. Anodised aluminium external wall with ventilators in the lamella spandrels. End walls clad with engineering bricks.   ↟ Ernst von Rudloff
465 Coal-promotion centre in Aachen. A naturally anodised aluminium framed curtain wall on the reinforced concrete skeleton. The aluminium lamellas are coated in a synthetic material.   ↟ Siegfried Reitz

463

464

466 Administrative building in Cologne-Sürth. External walls entirely clad with small ceramic mosaic. Naturally anodised aluminium windows with internal light metal Venetian blinds. Canopy and underside of the flat roof are in exposed concrete.   Å Esser

467

467 Section of the window façade of a bank administrative building in Düsseldorf. Curtain wall of 600 equal aluminium elements, each one-storey high and in sandwich construction, anodised a natural colour (Gartner).   Å Prof. Paul Schneider-Esleben

466

468 Central Bank of the Land of Northrhine Westphalia in Düsseldorf. Continuous bands clad with marble slabs (black labrador). Windows in polished aluminium; fixed parts silicon-grey, casement frames naturally anodised. Exposed supports on the *piano nobile* and the front faces of the canopy clad with aluminium; soffite timber boarded.   ⋀ Prof. Dr F. W. Kraemer
469 Section from a high administrative block of a camera works in Munich. Elements of the reinforced concrete frame painted. Infill panels of narrow split tiles in mellow colours.
⋀ G. H. Winkler
470 Office block in St Gallen/Switzerland. Bearing prefabricated concrete elements. Aluminium curtain wall, naturally anodised. Infill panels of coloured safety glass. Lamella blinds of stoved, glossed, light metal.   ⋀ Stäheli and Frehner

468

469

470

472a

472

472b

471 Industrial Management building in Essen. Light-metal curtain wall on a reinforced concrete frame. Infills and claddings of natural stone: Christallina Virginia, Dinbas and Shandong-granite (Zeidler and Wimmel).

𝄔 Prof. Dustmann

472 High office block of an insurance company (over a low level garage) in Essen. Reinforced concrete frame. Aluminium curtain wall. Infills and floor slabs are both clad with one panel: internally steel sheet, externally Polycolor glass. Concrete spandrels of the garage painted. Steel spiral staircase glossed (Herberts).

𝄔 Prof. Dr F. W. Kraemer

473 High insurance building in Frankfurt/Main. The projecting supports of the reinforced concrete frame are clad with copper. Aluminium curtain wall, anodised a bronze colour (Gartner). Infill elements of coloured glass.

Ⓐ Max Meid and Helmut Romeick

473

474 Administration block of a metal construction firm in Menzikon/ Switzerland. Curtain wall: aluminium infill elements a natural colour, cladding anodised dark grey blue. Ⓐ Hans Hauri

475 High block of a bank in Düsseldorf. Aluminium curtain wall, polished and anodised. Aluminium infill panels, anodised a natural grey colour (Gartner). Ⓐ Heinz Thoma

74

476 High administration block in Berlin. Exposed parts of the reinforced concrete frame painted. Front façades and infill areas clad with glass mosaic (Rogla Schalke). Aluminium windows.
⋏ Paul Schwebes and Dr Hans Schloszberger
477 Seagram building in New York. Steel curtain wall clad with bronze. Infill panels of enamelled steel sheet. ⋏ Mies van der Rohe

476a

476

(Continued from page 18)

means such as silicones, fluorides, emulsion paints and plastic skins are used. By these methods the surface achieves a water repellent skin, which precludes any possibility of capillary effects. Also under certain circumstances the damp diffusion is interrupted. In addition, the drying of the wall is slowed down; sulphates can be concentrated under the surface and having reached certain proportions, break away from the surface. If damp from inside cannot diffuse to the outside any more, the wall will be saturated with moisture from inside. Therefore the materials have to meet the following requirements:

1. Surface water must be repelled;
2. The damp diffusion has to be uninhibited;
3. Efflorescence of salts has to be prevented.

Workmanlike silicone impregnation normally meets these requirements. But firms with little experience in this field should not be entrusted with such work. After the solvent has evaporated, a thin skin of synthetic resin remains on the surface of the wall, which acts highly hydrophobically. The synthetic silicon resin also penetrates into the bricks and the mortar a few millimetres. The depth of penetration should be at least 5 mm in the mortar and 1·5 mm in the bricks. Also the openings, such as capillaries, remain around 98 per cent free, so that damp can escape. Walls with this treatment dry more quickly, so avoiding damage by damp, and assuring heat isolation for the rooms.

Paintwork on brick walls

On well-built brick walls paint is normally not necessary. But sometimes it is used for design or aesthetic reasons. Also a higher rain resistance can be achieved. With all paintwork one has to be sure that the brickwork still has the ability to balance moisture content. Paints which stop damp can lead to collection of water which not only causes damage to the paint, but also to the brickwork. In brickwork the water usually evaporates from the ends of capillaries. The capillary forces provide a steady supply of water coming to the surface. As soon as the capillary flow to the surface is broken, the rest of the damp is transported out by damp diffusion. Damp diffusion follows the temperature drop from inside to the outside.

Besides colourless (mainly impregnating) paint (i. e. paint which does not create a surface film) all other usual paints are feasible; these include chalk paints, cement paint, silicate or mineral paints, emulsion paints or white lime washes (for more information on painting see Section F). Oil paints, flat oil paints and synthetic resin paints are less advisable for external work because of their barrier effect.

For all mineral paints, the following rule has to be considered: only absorbent bricks are suitable for painting. If the brick does not absorb water when it is wettened, then it will not be suitable for this kind of paint. Alternatively, one must use organic paints. The suitability of the brick has to be tested if an emulsion paint is to be used. Especially in old buildings bricks can be found whose surface structure has been destroyed by the influence of weather, moisture or efflorescence. These bricks should be replaced, despite the fact that under certain conditions a penetrating paint can stop further textural decay. Cracked bricks or bricks with pores created by molten iron ore during firing should also be replaced as

neither cracks nor big pores of this kind can be closed by paints.

Facing bricks

Facing bricks (VHz) and facing bricks with vertical holes (VHLz) are frost-resistant bricks. Generally they are linked with the backing wall: then the whole section of the wall can be calculated statically. In external walls only bricks without cracks or damaged corners should be used.

Facing bricks are available with natural surfaces in different colours. The bricks are not vitrified and should be free of lumps of marl, lime or other materials which might cause efflorescence.

Facing bricks are available as solid bricks and bricks with holes in small size, normal size and special sizes. As bricks with vertical holes they have a unit weight of 1·2 to 1·4 kg/dm³ and as solid bricks up to 1·8 kg/dm³. Both kinds of brick reach a strength of 100 to 350 kg/cm².

Facing bricks, dependent on their type, can absorb water – for instance on the weather side. In good weather (little wind and no rain) they give off the water relatively quickly, water being quickly transported through the capillaries as the damp pressure from inside forces the moisture to the outside. In areas with much rain or wind the facing and backing walls have to be able to absorb a sufficient quantity of water. The thickness of the wall has to be chosen from this point of view and the construction adjusted to it (cavity walls).

Engineering bricks

In Germany, engineering bricks are available with (KHlz) and without (KMz) holes. Both kinds are available as thin and normal sizes; only the engineering brick with vertical holes is also supplied 1½ NF (i. e. 1½ times normal size).

KHlz and KMz types are burnt to the stage of vitrification; the average unit weight is 1·9 kg/dm³. As they are burnt almost to melting point they have a small volume of pores. The absorbing capacity for water penetrated into the joints is very small.

Because of their vitrification, engineering bricks are normally light in colour. By means of mineral or metallic admixtures to the clay other colours can be achieved, which range from blue-grey to red. As they have a constant strength and small tolerances in size, the accuracy of the brickwork can be very high.

Engineering bricks absorb practically no rainwater. Therefore they are normally used where a water-repellent surface is required. Then also the joints have to be water-resistant, as penetrated water – owing to the lack of capillary effect – can hardly be brought back to the surface. Drying out of the facing therefore is limited, and in heavy rain and wind the wall might experience moisture penetration. Heat insulation would be reduced and walls become moist.

Normally engineering bricks are dirt-repellent and under certain conditions acid-resistant, so they are very suitable for buildings which have to have low maintenance costs.

Because of their high weather-resistance they are often preferred to other facing materials. Their high strength (350 kg/cm²) also allows high loading, and contributes to the stiffness of the external wall.

Shallow engineering brick-tiles

Besides bricks as such a type of engineering brick-tile is also available, supplied as tiles with vertical holes or as solid tiles. The tiles have a depth of 5·2, 5·7 or 6·5 cm; they are also supplied in different heights. It is advisable to enquire from the brick manufacturers which sizes are available as the tiles are mostly produced in limited numbers. These tiles can be used in ways similar to engineering brick. Often they are used as so-called "economy facings" or fixed afterwards as weatherproofing of an external wall.

For the handling of these narrow tiles generally the same directions as for cladding in engineering bricks in double skin brickwork without air gap can be applied. These facing narrow tiles should be fixed to the roughcast backing wall with mortar of group II, as this provides good adhesion. Stainless wire anchors every fourth or fifth course of bricks connect the tiles to the wall behind.

It is important to use faultless tiles, as the insulating layer against weathering at 5·7 to 6·5 cm is much less than with normal engineering brick. No edges should be broken and long faces and ends have to be perfect. Careful transport to the site is advisable (by stacking on pallets). Because the tiles only serve the function of weather protection, the rest of the wall has to fulfil heat insulation requirements as well as a sufficient storage capacity for damp from the interior. Therefore it will cause difficulties if one uses a material for the backing wall which has not sufficient storage capacity. To improve the weather protection an insulating coat of bituminous or inorganic material is often placed between facing and backing walls. The same here as for the backing wall because it is mostly through the insulating layer that damp diffusion is stopped, or at least slowed down.

A proofing agent should be added to the jointing and pointing mortars. It is essential if a good water-repellent external wall is to be achieved that all joints be properly pointed. The surface can be impregnated afterwards with colourless silicone paint.

Tiles of standard brick proportion

These tiles are seldom used for external walls. They are suitable for flooring or for claddings on industrial buildings.

C Calcareous sandstones for external walls

These are produced from lime and a material containing a predominance of quartz. To bind lime and sand, water is added. Hardening of the stones is carried out in special boilers by means of steam pressure at temperatures of about 200° C.

DIN 106 is the standard for these stones. Solid stones, stones with holes and hollow blocks are produced. Solid stones can on their vertical section be reduced in area by up to 25 per cent.

As 1½ NF, the stones must have a handling slot 90 to 110 mm long by 30 to 45 mm wide (for hollow blocks, on the end face). As a tolerance, a single value of ±3 mm and a middle value of ±2 mm is permissible. The industry offers stones for external walls with a compression factor of 150 kp/cm² and 250 kp/cm². As an abbreviated description they bear the letter "V". For external walls only frost-resistant stones should be used. Coloured facings of calcareous sandstone are also available.

Hollow block calcareous sandstones cannot be used for facing work, because their compression factor of, at maximum, 75 kp/cm² is not adequate for external walls and in any case water pockets will form in view of the large number of holes. If the static requirements can be fulfilled, these stones are suitable for backing walls.

Calcareous sandstones have, if properly jointed, a consistent strength in every joint in view of their dimensional accuracy. However, on the exposed face, damaged stones should not be used.

In Germany, the Federal Union of the Calcareous Sandstone Industry Incorporated has published a pamphlet on exposed calcareous sandstones from which the extract on external wall protection is relevant:

"Even when the plinth is of exposed masonry, a 0·5 m coarse gravel strip or a paving stone used vertically should be applied in each case, so that when it rains the earth does not spray back and dirty the exposed masonry. The exposed masonry should be painted with a colourless silicone as far as possible on an undercoat of a solvent silicone. The silicone will prevent the penetration of damp in heavy rain and will reduce the wall's susceptibility to dirt by loosening the surface tension. However, the silicone must only be applied when the walling mortar and pointing mortar are well prepared. Before a silicone is applied to new masonry, free lime must be bound by fluorides. The application of silicone should where possible only be carried out by specialist firms; otherwise slightly irregular spotted silicone films occur when it rains, if the silicone is colourless.

If exposed masonry surfaces, which are badly marked or have been dirty a long time, are to be siliconised, then it is usually insufficient to clean the affected area with acetic acid. In such cases a steam-jet cleaning is of help. Sand jets should never be used. If the calcareous sandstones have been coated with clay for protection during erection, this will prove impossible to remove and therefore should never be used."

D External walls with ceramic split tiles

The material

Ceramic split tiles according to DIN 18166 are frost-resistant. They are produced in various colours, glazed and unglazed. As raw material, clays with or without mineral additions are used. The volumetric weight is 1·9 kg/dm³.

For standardized split tiles, frost-resistance, acid-resistance, impact-resistance, colour and lightfastness are guaranteed according to the efficiency requirements laid down in the standard. These tiles have ribs in a swallowtail form which ensure good adhesion to the mortar bed.

The preferred size is 245 x 120 mm. Split wall slabs are 13 to 20 mm thick. Deviations from the norm are admissible up to ±2 per cent. Special profiles are also available; mostly, however, they cost more to produce and there is a longer delivery period. Split slabs are usually tied together in parcels with steel bands. They are available in two qualities.

If they are supposed to be frost-resistant, split slabs are able to accept up to 6 per cent water. For buildings requiring acid resistance, water intake must not exceed 3 per cent. Bending strength should be at least 200 kg/cm². For the surface a hardening factor of at least 5 abrasion resistance (according to Mohs) is needed. Only unglazed slabs are acid- and alkali-resistant. Thermal expansion can be catered for in the joints. It is advisable to insert expansion joints.

A proposed cladding of split slabs should be considered in the planning stage of a building.

The slabs do form an effective protection against downpours of rain. At the same time, they do not permit the transmission of water vapour. The water vapour can only escape through the joints. A whole external wall clad with split slabs can adequately transmit water vapour: this transmission amounts to 10 to 20 per cent depending on the various sizes of slab and joint widths. For rooms which are damp it is advisable that the damp-laden internal air should be withdrawn or that a damp barrier backed with a thermal retention layer should be incorporated. In a one-layer wall construction the retaining layer should be between the internal plaster and the masonry, whilst in a multi-layer construction it should be fixed on the internal face of the thermal insulation.

Also in the category of coarse ceramic products are split engineering tiles. They are split after the baking process. This results in swallowtail-shaped fillets which allow good adhesion with the mortar when the tiles are being laid.

An essential advantage of this material is its good resistance to weather effects, dirt and mechanical stresses.

These tiles also have the appearance and properties of engineering bricks. They are produced in a thin format and a normal format. There are also so-called decorative formats. Special tiles are produced to fit corners and for the top and bottom courses.

Each brickworks, however, delivers variable tiles: the thickness of the tile is also not uniform. There are tiles with exposed areas according to DIN 105 which are 16 or 20 mm thick. The thickness of these slabs remains constant, it is only the length or height which varies.

When a wall is clad with split tiles the finished parts must fit exactly the parts still to be faced.

If the split tiles are to be fixed directly on the wall, they, together with the mortar, must take on the function of protection against rain. Even in strong winds only small amounts of water can reach the backing wall and associated materials, when the slabs and joints are impervious. When there is intrusive sunshine strong tension results as a consequence of the relatively high thermal conductivity of the split tiles and of their slight expansionability. This load can, however, in essence be taken by the joints between the slabs.

Damp diffusion is hindered by the impervious material. Provided the backing wall and its associated materials have sufficient storage capacity this does not appear to be objectionable chiefly because the joints can also give off part of the water vapour externally.

It is advisable to draw off the water vapour from damp rooms (these could even include, under unfavourable circumstances, kitchens and bathrooms) where the walls are already saturated with such water vapour from the interior. The former can best be achieved by a ventilated skin or by an extract fan.

Application

The adhesion of split slabs is essentially affected by the roughness of the surface, the absorptive capacity and the stability of the backing wall. The backing wall must be of such a firmness that it can bear the weight of the slabs and accept tensions. Good adhesion of the mortar is achieved if the surface is very rough. On the other hand if the surface of the wall is smooth and it has a great absorptive capacity, direct application of the split tiles is inadvisable. For then water is drawn too rapidly from the mortar so that it is unable to achieve adequate cohesion with the backing wall. Even a backing wall which can only accept a small amount of water is unsuitable because the mortar is then only inadequately held. If thermal retention layers are built on to the external face, then direct application of tiles is definitely not advised. Under certain circumstances an improved adhesion can be achieved by stretching wire mesh across the surface. However it is then more expedient to anchor the mesh. In such cases it is safer to stretch a constructional steel mesh across the face and to apply the slabs after a coat of render. Obviously the constructional steel mesh must be firmly anchored to the backing wall.

If calcareous sandstones, pumice stones or lightweight concrete are to be clad, then the tiles should never be applied until the shrinking in those materials has ended.

Fundamentally, two processes are possible:

1. Tiles applied directly to the wall;
2. Tiles applied on mesh.

The first process can be used if on the external wall sufficient adhesion for a mortar of mortar group III can be achieved. Traditionally, split tiles were not completely pointed so that hollow spaces could form between the tiles and the backing wall. These stored water from outside or damp from inside so that water pockets could form. This led to damage by saturation or else in winter the tiles would fall off.

Proofing agents in the mortar are not always advisable in such applications. Through these, partly soluble salts cannot be separated or, ultimately, water which has penetrated cannot be taken up by the mortar bed or the backing wall. Thus the storage capacity is reduced. Consequently a complete change was made to applying the split tiles when fully saturated. The GT fully-saturated process is the best. There are the thin and thick bed processes.

The thin bed process

The backing wall must have all loose bits thoroughly brushed away and the joints must be well raked out and prepared. Saturated wall surfaces, dirty and oil-smeared concrete walls, and frozen areas of walls cannot be clad. It has proved advisable first of all to render the backing wall with render at least 2 mm and no more than 5 mm thick. The sand should be sharp-grained, 1 to 5 mm, and for one part cement there should be 4 or 5 parts sand. This render, by increasing the roughness of the surface, provides better cohesion between tiles and backing wall.

If this backing wall has considerably loosened up, then render (mortar group III) should be applied 1 or 2 cm thick. Then the mortared tiles are set into this fresh render. At any one time only the area which is to be clad immediately with tiles should be rendered. In the mortaring process special attention should be paid to filling the swallowtail to ensure its proper fitting. The joints should be 8 to 10 mm wide.

The bedding mortar consists of one part cement and 4 to 5 parts sand of grain size 0 to 3 mm. Ultimately, tufa can also be added: but then the proportion of sand should also be increased. If lime is added to the mortar, it should only be high hydraulic lime. Approximately half an hour after the tile-laying, a start can be made on the pointing. The split engineering tiles should be pointed at least 1 cm deep with plastic mortar of mortar group III which has a 20 to 25 per cent proportion of fine sand. Thus in this method the render, the bedding mortar and the pointing mortar can set simultaneously. Corners and other special forms can be built in at the same time.

When the job is finished the wall must be protected against downpours of rain and sunshine as under certain circumstances the joints could be washed out or the pointing mortar can burn.

The thick bed process

All the procedures for this method are fundamentally the same as for the thin bed process. The only difference lies in the mortaring of the tiles. They are put into a simple former (planks or slabs with side fillets) with the finished face placed down. However, on account of the fillets, the side edges are so high that after the swallowtail has been filled with mortar it is completely covered to a depth of 1·5 to 2 cm. After the surplus mortar has been wiped off, the tiles are taken individually from the former and placed in position.

In buildings with greater variabilities of expansion in the external wall the surface adhesion of the hard skin would possibly have led to tensions and damage. Consequently larger cladding panels were developed which are fixed on anchors or toggles in the backing wall. When transferring split engineering tiles to panels, the following should be considered:

The face must have a wire mesh stretched across it which has a mesh size of 3 to 5 cm: alternatively a constructional steel mesh could be fixed at a distance of 1 cm in front of the backing wall. The mesh should be anchored to the backing wall. Mortar dabs of mortar group III are used as spacers between mesh and backing wall and then the mesh is rough rendered 2 to 2·5 cm thick. Area by area the split tiles are then set with fully saturated mortaring into the render. The anchors for fixing the tiles must be of non-ferrous metals. The prefabricated tiles' areas should not be greater than 6 to 8 m². These panels should be separated from one another by expansion joints which should penetrate to the backing wall. The joints should be filled with a lasting mastic. For panels which go round corners a vertical expansion joint must occur in the corner zone.

The good appearance of an external wall with split engineering tiles depends essentially on the formation of the joints and the proper cleaning of the tiles. A minimum joint width of 8 to 10 mm guarantees the necessary density. If the tiles are to be pointed afterwards, the water content of the pointing mortar should be kept as low as possible. The mortar should be mean so that it does not shrink. By the addition of tufa the mortar does indeed become water-repellent and more elastic but it simultaneously delays the hardening process. The colour of the pointing should give a muted effect because light-coloured joints in the façade can easily become dirty. It is inadvisable to use cements with a high gypsum content ("marble cement"). If sealing agents (Biber, Cerinol, Dichtulit, Ceresit, for example) are added, the instructions for application must be precisely adhered to. Bituminous intermediary insulations should be avoided.

In general one should clean with water, and only if the façades are very dirty should they be cleaned with an acetic acid solution of 1 : 20. Hydrochloric acid solutions are unsuitable since they are likely to cause efflorescence.

Expansion joints in the main body of the building must not be covered with tiles but should be closed with an elastic material. In ceramic cladding, expansion joints should be provided so that tensions as a result of thermal stress can be catered for. Particularly wide temperature variations often occur on western fronts. Furthermore the colour tone of the tiles also affects the temperature. A temperature difference between the surface of the tiles and the surrounding air can amount to 20° C for light grey tiles and 40° C for black tiles. If the masonry behind this is only 10° cooler, temperature variations up to 50° can occur. Light grey tiles, with an 80° temperature difference have an expansion of 0·32 mm/m whilst black tiles, with a 100° temperature difference can expand 0·4 mm/m.

Where thermal retention slabs are built on to the rear side of the split tiles, a heat vapour can occur as a result of poor thermal conductivity. In this case ventilation is the remedy. Horizontal expansion joints should be arranged at floor height: surfaces without an expansion joint should not exceed 16 to 20 m². The joints themselves must penetrate in normal joint width to the backing and be closed off by a lasting mastic, plastic joint bands or sealing strips. One can also well seal off clad façades with felt strips which are stuck into the joint. If for visual reasons a broad band is not desired, insertion strips could be considered or the strips could be built in straightaway whilst the wall is under construction.

Split tiles on aerated concrete elements

1. Aerated concrete walls must be brushed clean before the split tiles are applied and then they must be thoroughly dampened, for example with a hose, so that the necessary binding dampness will not be drawn out by the mortar.
2. The prepared aerated concrete walls are completely coated with rough render which should consist of one part normal cement and four parts sharp grained sand, if possible washed, of graining 1 to 5 mm.
3. The setting of the split tiles should not be carried out until 12 hours after the rough render has been applied.
4. For large unbroken areas on multi-storey buildings it is imperative that the entire area of the wall should be covered with a mortar mesh. It is advantageous to insert the anchors in the masonry during the actual construction. As reinforcement: constructional steel mats or wide ribbed sheet of netting. The anchoring irons have to be able to bear the weight of the split tile cladding, including the mortar bed, of

about 70 kg/m² and thus must be correspondingly distributed in strength and number. The anchoring irons must be rust free or they must be coated. If unprotected anchors are used a covering coat of rough render should be applied to them before the tiles are laid.

5. Between the rough render and the layer of split tiles there should be used a binding layer of mortar of the same mixing proportions given under paragraph 2. The thickness of the mortar bed should above be on average 15 mm.

6. Only a restricted number of tile courses should be laid one above the other, otherwise there is the danger that the lowest courses (which are not sufficiently set) will be pushed out of true because of too heavy a loading.

7. Expansion joints in the main body of the building must not be closed by a layer of tiles. Expansion joints should be provided within the facing of split tiles in order to cater for tensions which are produced through the elasticity of the individual parts of the building (columns or supporting beams) caused by the influence of temperature, which creates contraction or expansion, or yet again by movement in the concrete resulting from shrinking or creeping. In the arrangement of the expansion joints one customarily separates, in buildings with steel or reinforced concrete skeletons, the area of the columns from the area of the supporting beams, by means of vertical or horizontal joints at each floor level. If the form of the building does not permit such an arrangement, then the expansion joints in aerated concrete walls (with a recognised higher thermal retention) must run vertically at intervals of 3 to 4 m. These specifications are also applicable to aerated concrete masonry buildings.

8. Amongst the advantages which a cladding of split tiles offers is certainly a technically faultless form of construction. (In especially well-sponsored cases the Advice Bureaux of the manufacturers make themselves available.)

The pointing

In an investigation undertaken by Prof. Dr Ing. Albrecht, Stuttgart, and Dr Ing. Schneider, Stuttgart, on the water permeability of ceramic split tile claddings on external walls, the pointing mortar was also described and the following comments were made:

"The permeability of ceramic wall tile claddings can be traced back to the porosity of the joints. It occurs through cracks in the pointing mortar which are caused by the shrinking of a too finely grained mortar. With pointing mortar of an appropriate composition it has proved possible to produce joints which to a considerable extent are both free of cracks and impervious. The results of these experiments can be summarized as follows:

a) A water-impervious pointing mortar for wall tile claddings should be composed of mixed grain sizes. The proportion of fine grains (up to 0·2 mm diameter) and the mortar materials (including the cement) should be between 25 and 55 per cent of the weight. The greatest impermeability proved to be in mortars with a fineness figure of between 1·5 and 2·5 (reckoned by evaluating what remained in the sieve). Outside these limits, the mortars were porous on account of cracking.

b) If pointing mortar is to be impervious it should not contain too much binding agent. The mortars with the best results

were those with a mixed proportion, cement to filler, of 1 : 4 or 1 : 3 parts. A customary trade ready-mixed mortar also proved to be waterproof. The latter's mixing proportions could well lie within the acceptable limits. However, the mixing proportion 1 : 0·5 and 1 : 2 had too much cement and because of cracking was pervious.

c) To treat the pointing mortar with a pointing tool has proved to be of no advantage.

d) By the addition of p.v.a. the capillary intake of water was reduced. This additive would also reduce the formation of cracks. However, the permeability of the joints was not markedly reduced.

e) A stearate additive likewise produced a reduction of capillary water intake. It was not possible to ascertain an influence on the permeability of the pointing mortar.

It follows that the waterproofing of the pointing is not conditioned either by the capillary structure of the pointing mortar (i. e. its absorptive capacity and permeability) or by its solidity. It is imperative that cracking be avoided if the joint is to be waterproof. The experiments have shown that this is possible by, as above mentioned, limiting the fineness of the sand and by limiting the content of binding agent. Further experiments to narrow the limits are in progress."

One can conclude that it is possible to produce pointing mortar for wall claddings which, applied in the usual way, will withstand downpours of rain, effectively waterproofing the wall.

Assembly – external wall panels with split tiles

Ceramic material is also used in the prefabrication of large wall slabs: split tiles, medium size mosaic, and fine mosaic. The tiles are placed in the former and concrete poured over. By this means the time-consuming job of setting ceramic tiles on the site is dispensed with. The panels are placed in position by means of cranes.

Italy and France have had these large panels with ceramic facing for some time because prefabricated building began earlier in these countries. In Paris, blocks of flats were built with façade panels in concrete and medium size mosaic which were 2·80 x 4·00 m. The German prefabricated elements industry also provides such panels. Amongst others, insulating panels of Durasol with medium size mosaic are produced. In Switzerland this process has been used for some time. The siliconising of wood fibreboard and the after-treatment were very important because it was necessary to achieve panels which could be dimensionally controlled. Panels of 10 cm thick Durasol were also already in production and in use with medium size mosaic on their external face. The panels were 0·62 x 1·80 m. On the site these panels were fixed to a steel skeleton and the separation joints were filled with mastic.

Split tiles are similarly joined to concrete in the negative process. In this process the cladding is at the same time cast with the main concrete mass. The density of pointing mortar in this process is very high so that the entry of moisture from outside is much restricted. By doing this the danger of efflorescence is much reduced. The process: inside a prestressed concrete mould (acting as a supporting slab) one places an adhesive layer and on to that the split tiles are placed and pressed in through a grid. The visual face lies so tightly on it that when the concrete is poured the visual face cannot become soiled. The slabs can be produced according to the size of the constructional element. These panels are delivered on slabs. If there are intermediate supports they must lie absolutely flat. When stacking them they must lie horizontally. During transport they must not bow because otherwise under certain circumstances they could spring off in the direction of the workman erecting them.

The slabs which are particularly suitable for poured concrete are delivered in the following sizes: 0·50 x 1·50 m, 0·50 x 0·75 m, 1·00 x 1·50 m, 1·00 x 0·75 m. They weigh between 45 and 60 kg/m². Recently, narrow tiles and split tiles have also been linked to prefabricated slabs without a supporting layer. The tiles are then glued to an element by means of special adhesives (liquid resins or sealing agents). As the sealers (for example Phenoplaste) can be coloured, the joints can be coloured at will. Process: the tiles are placed face down in the form. The joint grid is stuck on to the supporting slab by means of an organic plant adhesive. This adhesive strip prevents the surface faces of the tiles being soiled during the sealing process. Gypsum or cement plugs are pressed into the joints as spacers. The prefabricated panels are about 1 m²: they are fixed to the wall with anchors of various types. The elements are so arranged that there is an air gap between them and the wall: the ventilation makes it possible to leave open some intermediate horizontal joints on the lowest and topmost panels. The connecting joints between the panels are produced in the same material on their work face as the joints in the panel itself.

This pointing is everlastingly flexible so that any ultimate movement in the wall can be taken up. The panel can be placed in front of any backing wall because the wall material has no bearing on the matter.

E External walls with fine ceramic material

Medium size and small mosaic

Fine ceramic wall claddings have been increasingly used in recent years. However, the panels of medium and small mosaic, prefabricated in tile works, are now more frequently built into the external wall on the site. Common sizes:

	Medium size mosaic	Strip mosaic	Combi-mosaic	Small mosaic
Size of the individual tiles	4,2 x 4,2 cm	4,2 x 2,0 cm	4,2 x 4,2 cm 4,2 x 2,0 cm 2,0 x 2,0 cm	2,0 x 2,0 cm
Size of prefabricated panels	52,6 x 30,6 cm	35,0 x 35,0 cm	35,0 x 35,0 cm	35,0 x 35,0 cm

Small mosaic consists of sintered stone material and is usually unglazed. Such a surface is resistant to frost. The combination of medium and small mosaic (combi-mosaic) is characterized by its colour variations and because of size variation the joints are irregular.

The mosaic pieces are either stuck face down on to paper, which can be stripped off with water after fixing, or their reverse side is stuck down either on to a woven fabric of jute, perlon or punched paper, or on to strips of synthetic material which are inserted in the mortar bed.

On the site the panels, which weigh from 10 to 11 kg/m², are laid by means of two processes in the preferable mortar bed, or in the socalled thin bed process: the wall is first rendered plumb, its surface being then completely flat, yet it must still be rough. In the second process the panels are not fixed with cement mortar but with hydraulic or normally drying mortar or, yet again, adhesive. With this new method, 10 to 15 per cent of the processing costs can be saved. Moreover, the tile-layer has an easier job, since he needs neither to straighten the surface nor to consider the alignment of the joints. All he has to do when laying tiles is to check the joint arrangement.

If tiles are laid by the old method, synthetic emulsion is added so that the mortar achieves a greater adhesive strength. The tiles should not be put in water first. Rather one should pre-coat the side to be laid with an emulsion and water mix 1 : 1; this pre-coat must then be allowed to dry. To the laying mortar of cement and dry sand (1 : 1) should be added PC1-Emulsion and water (1 : 1) and the whole mixed until it is suitable for the trowel. This mortar can be thinly coated either on the side of the pieces to be laid or on the base; then the mosaic pieces are pressed into the fresh mortar and adjusted. This adhesive mortar will remain plastic long enough for this to be done. For small jobs it is sufficient to stick the pieces with the appropriate adhesive, though of course the surface must then definitely be plumb. Special adhesives are spread about 1 to 2 mm thick onto the base or onto the pieces with a toothed scraper. Then the mosaic is pressed firmly in.

The joints, about 1 mm thick, are filled up with a joint mortar or joint mastic on a synthetic material base. For this job a rubber disc or a sponge is used. Mixed mortar remains usable for two hours. Joint mastic is sold in tubes in various colours and is ready to use. The mastic is pressed into the joints by means of a nylon nozzle. If a joint is not smooth enough, it can be drawn out again with a wet cloth if done immediately. Any smudges of mastic must be removed straightaway.

Picture mosaic

Picture mosaic can also be prefabricated, stuck on to paper or on to a rigid board and delivered to the site. The areas intended for the mosaic must be recessed and rough-rendered with a cement render; if the picture is to be flush with the rest of the façade then the thickness of the mosaic (5 to 7 mm including the adhesive) must be considered. Newly developed tile adhesives stick even on a damp base. This is very important for picture mosaics because the width of the joints must be very exactly checked. This mosaic is also laid in the thin bed process. Mortar residue is best removed at once because later it is both difficult and time-consuming to do.

Tiles of stone material

Such tiles, known also as floor or mosaic tiles may be counted amongst ceramic floor tiles; they are mainly used only on plinths or as column cladding. They can be baked at temperatures of up to 900° C and are consequently very firm and resistant to frost and acid. Generally they are used unglazed. As a mosaic cladding – 20 or 50 mm² – they have a relatively good transmission of the internal condensation through the joints on account of their joint network. The tiles take in water at the rate of 1 to 2 per cent of their weight and they have a bending strength of 250 kg/cm². In most cases the base is given a coat of cement mortar. According to some recent experiments, however, it is possible to lay the tiles in the thin bed process. Suitable agents are those setting hydraulically such as Latex, artificial resin and mixed adhesives.

F Rendered external walls (coloured mortar and render to be painted)

Constructional/technical prerequisites

In any architectural building with rendered areas, the problem is whether the desired colour effect will last for long enough and can, on occasion, be easily renewed.

When faultless render has been painted, the ageing period of technical and visual durability in a town atmosphere should usually not last more than six years: one reckons on a rather longer period for coloured render. This demands high weather resistance and the most effective possible rejection of dirt. The latter is especially caused by industry, by airborne fine ash in densely populated areas where open fires are used or in the vicinity of railways, or yet again by dust thrown up by traffic and carried by rain. The formation of dirt can be reduced even at the planning stage if the following precautions are taken:

1. The smoother a surface, the more a building lies in the path of dirt carried by wind. The surface should be so executed, from the point of view of structure and material technique, that it has as effective as possible a dirt-resistant surface (possibly with the assistance of additives).

2. Avoidance or limitation of ornamental horizontal elements – projections, sills and chamfers.

3. Reduction of dirt carried by rain by means of over-sailing roofs, cantilevering upper floors.

4. Especially prone areas should have dirt-resistant cladding in place of rendered areas.

5. Appropriate surface water disposal so that draining rain and dew do not run over rendered areas. Balconies and parapets require gutters or non-rusting sheet flashings.

Some of the especially important questions which crop up in day-to-day practice are here indicated:

Window junctions: it is astonishing how many defective walls still come about simply because the window sills are badly made. So that dripping rain water can be kept away from the rendered areas beneath the windows, and likewise not be forced onto the wall by strong winds, there must be an adequate nosing drip. A nosing has the effect of causing the water to drip off and not to run back on the underside of the sill to the wall junction: a shallow groove will not achieve this result. To prevent water running off sideways and forming rain streaks because of the dust it contains, the side overhang should be correspondingly large and the sill at that point should have a slight fall towards the window opening. There is no point in rendering over the flashings, because the metal

expands so much in heat that the render breaks away. The joint between the sheet and the render must, however, be protected so that at that point no water can penetrate which would otherwise lead to damage by damp or frost. The following solution, although rather cumbersome, is nevertheless technically fool-proof: the render is led down in the internal reveal to the arched flashing. From this point onwards it is wedge-shaped so the sheet can move freely, and simultaneously the joint between sheet and render is adequately safe-guarded. It is then impossible for rain to be driven into this joint.

Gutter boards; ancillaries such as porches; plinth: for these parts of a building the same principles apply. The covering of projecting parts of a building must have an adequate fall and the joint between render and covering must be formed as suggested for window openings. The damming up of damp must be avoided at all costs.

It is futile to render the walls of inhabited buildings right down to ground level. To avoid damage by frost, damp from the ground should not be able to rise either in the render itself or in the render base. Thus for rendering plinths, only a mortar of group III is appropriate, one which hardly absorbs and which is very stable.

Since the plinth needs to be especially resistant, a more suitable material is frequently used, e.g. facing brickwork of synthetic or natural masonry or a bush-hammered concrete. Damp must not be allowed to dam up in the plinth either. The plinth should therefore be recessed about 1 cm but never project.

Gutter and fall pipe arrangements: all installations intended to receive water and drain it should be so generously dimensioned that they do not overflow even in heavy rain. The fall pipe should be fixed immediately after the external render has been finished so that the fresh render is not damaged if there is sudden rain: if render is discoloured because of thorough saturation, this can never be remedied and remains noticeable even if painted afterwards. Occasionally the following expedient can be used to drain off part of a roof: a pipe with guaranteed no-spray or dripping terminal is taken down internally.

The application of render for subsequent painting

Simple scaffolding systems in which the scaffold poles are erected adjacent to the masonry are unsuitable for rendering: they would enforce horizontal rendering sections since one can only work up from the lower scaffolding if the upper one is demounted. Until recently the just-finished rendered area, especially in the warm season, would have tightened up so much that it was hardly still possible to finish off the joints. Hence the scaffolding must definitely stand free of the wall, in fact at a distance of about 30 cm, so that it is possible to work behind the poles without difficulty. If all the scaffolding platforms are in use at the same time the renderers are staggered diagonally one beneath the other. They can work together: the fresh edges can be carefully rubbed one into the other so that no gaps occur. This method of working also makes it possible to site the joints now running vertically at points where they will not be visible, i.e. on the corners, at projections from the building, expansion joints and rainwater pipes. In most cases it will be necessary to arrange for the whole area to be rendered.

Freestanding scaffold systems are also indispensable where walls are 24 cm thick and constructed of hollow blocks of above average dimensions. When the poles are being put on the masonry, holes must be knocked in the blocks. This causes the air gaps, necessary for thermal insulation, to be lost at those points because when the scaffolding holes are later closed up, the original voids are filled up too. Thus cold bridges would result there or points with a different absorption capacity to the remainder of the area. It must be realized that in some cases the scaffolding holes will later appear dark whilst in others they will make a light contrast in the rendered area.

Rendering technique

Mortar can be applied either by hand or with a machine, but since good adhesion of the mortar with a rendered ground and the individual layers one with the other is dependent on the method of application the latter is obviously of great significance for the permanence of the render. First of all the weather conditions should be considered; these can call for special precautions for the protection of the fresh render. In the application itself, the following fundamental rules should particularly be considered:

The application of mortar by hand: the mortar must be firmly thrown with the trowel so that it penetrates into all the unevennesses of the render ground. It will only stick well if the air has been withdrawn from the surface pores and if the pores have been filled with a grout or binding agent. This cannot be achieved by merely smoothing on the mortar with the board. A mortar so applied would certainly have bad adhesion with a rendered surface which has only a weak absorptive capacity. The individual layers of render must be uniformly applied so that in themselves they are both equally thick and dense. It is difficult to continue work on layers of mortar which vary in thickness, because they mature at different rates: where the mortar is still too soft, it dissolves itself when it chafes against the undersurface and there will be a hollow at that point after hardening. But if one waits until the thicker layer has matured then the thinner one cannot be treated any more.

The thickness of the individual layer of render is dictated by the size of the largest sand grain. In one application the mortar should only be applied in a thickness which will have good adhesion. A good rule of thumb to decide on this thickness is to multiply the diameter of the largest grain by three. The next layer can be applied when the previous one has hardened to such an extent that it can bear the next one. Particular care should then be taken if various mortar groups are used for the individual layers. In such cases soft should never be worked into soft; this requirement is especially valid for roughcast, which must have sufficiently hardened so that it cannot be wiped from the undersurface by hand when the first coat of render is applied. To achieve perfect adhesion for the top coat of render, the undercoat should be roughed up: this is best achieved with a saw blade which should be scraped in horizontal waves.

The application of mortar by machine: for application by machine there are numerous appropriate pieces of equipment which throw the mortar with equal force as in the trowel process. Additionally, rollers, centrifugal machines, or compressed air nozzles are used. Usually the mortar which is to be applied by machine must be especially carefully made up. This holds above all for the choice of sand in order to prevent disturbances during the mortar transport and throwing. Since the mortar is intensively mixed again in the equipment it is very pliant when being applied, even though the proportion of binding agent is of the usual standard. A characteristic of the machine application of mortar is that it is applied equally firmly and in several thin layers one after the other. By this means good adhesion is achieved even with a surface which has poor absorptive capacity. Economically, rendering by machine is far superior to hand rendering, for the cost of wages is radically reduced and, simultaneously, larger areas can be rendered. The level of increased efficiency depends not only on the machine used but also on the size and form of the building and on the dividing up of the areas to be rendered.

Render bases. Kinds of render: at the planning stage it must be decided what kind of external wall is to be used and whether its surface is to be painted. If it is to be painted, certain regulations should be considered if a spotted or irregular painted surface and premature ageing phenomena are to be avoided:

a) Mixed masonry consisting of elements of varying absorptive capacities gives a rendering surface in which, after painting, bricks which have greater absorption cause a lighter or darker contrast according to their colour.

b) The rendering base must not have any wide open joints which would have to be bridged over by the render. These would later cause cracks in the render which would make the wall joint obvious and even after painting would still be visible. (Despite the fact that today there are numerous possibilities for "patching up" fine render cracks in fresh coats of paint, the rendering should be carried out no less carefully.)

c) Woodwool light constructional slabs are only suitable for bearing render when the slabs are compound and are sufficiently carefully secured to the supporting structure by means of strips of wire netting. If this is not done, damage to the render and consequently to the paint is unavoidable.

d) Too thin a layer of external render permits the outline of the masonry joints to show through. Paint does not blot them out: in variable damp conditions, the phenomenon occurs again even if it originally began to disappear.

No economies should be made on the external render if the render is to be painted. Time and time again it has been proved that a thoroughly careful application of paint cannot neutralize or compensate for defects in the undersurface. Even if for a short time (perhaps until the time of setting even) the surface appears perfect, the consequences of an inadequate undersurface usually soon make themselves apparent. Laymen – in this context even architects, building technicians and officials can often be included – frequently blame either the paint or the painter for these faults. However, on closer examination it often turns out that it was the undersurface which was at fault. Thus, from the point of view of economics also, the areas to be painted should be prepared with the utmost care. Fortunately, there is now a noticeable tendency to use mortars of groups Ib or II (hydraulic lime mortar, high hydraulic lime cement mortars) for external areas which are to be painted.

The composition and surface structure of the render must be made up in such a way that they will take paint. The renderer can, as is well known, carry out fine and coarse grain renders which are of very different composition and by this means create smooth or rough areas. Surface effects of variable structure can stand side by side on the same building in order to achieve variations in the visual effect. Such variable render bases however should not be treated straightaway with the same paint or with the same painting technique.

Rendering in the cold season: if night frosts are expected, external renders should not be made up. Every kind of fresh mortar, high in water content, would be burst open by frost and would then flake off. Since the structure of the mortar would then be destroyed and could not be reinstated, the render would have to be completely renewed. If the frost is only short-lived, only the upper layer is damaged: the lower layers of render retain their normal firmness. In the cold season therefore rendering should only be done externally if one can assume that it will set and thoroughly dry out before temperatures drop below freezing point. Consequently, during the winter, a building should only be clad externally if it can be well covered (by means of some protective construction) and be heated until the render has hardened sufficiently. Nevertheless the danger of frost damage is so great that it is worth waiting for the appropriate weather before rendering.

Rendering in the warm season: external rendering should not take place in heavy rain. Continuous downpours saturate the render base to such an extent that the pores of the masonry cannot absorb any more water from the mortar and the latter then slides off, or at least has bad adhesion.

It is therefore advisable to wait until the render base has dried out somewhat.

Heavy rain also damages the surface and can even impair the structure of fresh render: this is then, after hardening, excessively porous. Downpours can even wash away fresh render. Hydraulic mortars as well must harden for a while, undisturbed in the air, before they can be exposed to adverse conditions. So that the render can harden without hindrance, can retain the necessary dampness for this, and does not develop shrinkage cracks, the mortar should not be allowed to dry out too quickly through wind, sun or high air temperatures. This is especially true for hydraulic mortars. Thus, if there is strong sunshine, it has proved valuable to protect the areas to be rendered by means of sunshades and to keep the fresh render damp for long enough by spraying it with water.

Paints on external walls

Paints on rendered external walls can be applied today with materials of widely differing types. Inorganic and organic paint agents have proved themselves sufficiently permanent if their manufacture is properly suited to the limitations of the paint undersurfaces as well as the climatic and atmospheric conditions. Above all, for newly rendered areas, the prerequisite for a perfect finish is a careful matching up between the properties of the undersurface and the overoptimistic claims plus the actual properties of the paint.

When applying paint externally on to newly rendered areas, the following fundamental stipulations should be considered:

a) All surface treatments should above all withstand the test of weathering conditions which are different in the country from the town and again are different in valleys from hills, etc. The stresses which today inflict themselves on paint in densely populated towns must be regarded as normal wear and tear and for which a paint intended for external work must absolutely live up to its claims. Furthermore, it is already realized that today's exhaust gases are not only considerably denser than at the beginning of our century, but also contain considerably more chemical agents. Just the increase in the burning of coke, coal and oil alone (formerly more wood and briquettes were burnt) contributes considerably to this situation. To this can be added further aggressive agents from waste industrial gases and from cars, as well as the additional formation of dust caused by these.

The more the surface of the building is attacked by the atmosphere and the more dirt is carried by the atmosphere, the more resistant and dirt-repellent the paint undersurfaces and the paints themselves must be. With increasing air pollution, smoother paint surfaces will be preferred, whilst in open countryside or on the edges of conurbations surface structures which are less smooth will be appropriate, chiefly because wind and weather here have a naturally cleansing effect and bear hardly any dirt.

b) The less one has to reckon with dirt deposits or premature ageing on the external surfaces of buildings, the sooner light coloured paints can be considered suitable. On the other hand whilst heavy air pollution continues and the adverse effect of agents carries on, medium or dark coloured paints will frequently be preferred because dirt does not show so quickly or so disagreeably on these colours.

c) In practice, certain consequences have resulted from the above factors which should be judged on their merits. Thus, experience has frequently taught us that it is far wiser to choose smooth surfaces to start with, rather than rough surface effects, chiefly because the latter are more prone to becoming dirty. Coarse or rough surfaces are particularly unsuitable on the so-called weather sides because they are far more liable to deposits of dirt. Additional precautions are also necessary for those rendered areas which require "breathing activity". On the weather sides, paints which are especially weather-repellent or paints which have a supplementary water-proofing are advisable. This is particularly important at points which are excessively exposed to downpours of rain.

d) At the necessary cost-evaluation stage for a new building, one naturally keeps asking oneself the question whether it might be possible to retain reserves for internal finishes at the expense of certain economies on the surface treatment of the exterior. As a representative "simple finish" one could take a mean render painted with lime if one intends a few years later to recoat with a better paint. However, paints which are too simply applied are not an adequate protection for the render. Furthermore, repainting carried out relatively soon will cost a considerable sum (renewed scaffolding, etc.). Nowadays there is such a wide choice of external paints, each with differing characteristics and suitability, that one should aim to choose the one which, according to its merits, is really the best suited for the job and not attempt to standardize the paint application. The architect should inform himself about specific brands by consulting a well-versed, independent specialist. Mason and renderer should both be told about the kind of paint intended before they begin their work so that the right type of mortar is selected. The painter should be informed about the type of mortar used, because a render of mortar group Ia cannot be painted with dispersion paints before the elapse of a certain period. If mortar groups Ib and II are used, this stipulation no longer applies. The presence of proofing agents in the render must also be considered when the paint is being chosen.

e) In normal ageing it has been established that a properly renewed coat of paint, if it is carried out at the appropriate time for the type of paint, will usually cost a relatively small amount. But one should not wait too long and then have to select a type which is favourable for a deteriorated surface; even when applying a new coat of paint one can aim at appropriate reconditioning factors. The total result is that without exception it is the carrying out of the job, the proper and conscientious preparation of the undersurface and the application of the external paints, which count for more than the properties and suitability of the materials used. Nowadays, the latter are available in great numbers; however, they all require the knowledge of the thoroughly versed specialist for their application.

All the following paints, which are briefly discussed, have one common factor: their thinning and particle dispersion agent is water. Nevertheless, with regard to their very variable characteristics and suitability, a clear division is necessary into inorganic-mineral and organic paints.

Paints with mineral agents (lime pigments, silicone pigments, cement pigments)

In present-day practice, façade paints should not only serve the function of protecting and embellishing the surface, but should also contribute to regulating the "breathing" of the masonry. On account of the considerably reduced wall strength in present-day buildings, paints which are too porous or too dense (sealing) cannot be used. The lime pigment of the old-fashioned type was such a porous paint, whilst the linseed oil type (matt oil types, etc.) are amongst those paints which form a strong film and thus they seal off too efficiently. The fundamental requirement of a paint which permits the exchange of water vapour (to the exterior as well as to the interior) is consequently indispensable for walls of relatively low strength. This requirement is particularly valid if, for example, the layers of render are no longer the traditional thickness of 20 mm but only about 15 mm. Lime pigment was for a long time a very popular coating for rendered areas, and it is still used today in the country in southern Germany. But such a coating often does not last sufficiently any more. The increase in air pollution with its sulphur content has a particularly destructive effect on lime pigments as soon as damp appears as well and forms sulphuric acid. (The renders also suffer from such chemical reactions.) As a result, more stable mineral paints were developed, which are partly improved lime pigments. As these new paints are of greater importance than the unmodified lime pigments, it is not necessary to go into detail about the latter type.

Whitewashes and lime renders: amongst the various new possibilities for treating external areas with white or coloured pigments, the whitewash and lime render processes have gained considerable importance. This can be explained by the chemical relationship of the materials used in this process, with the render. The paints are ready to use and contain, apart from chalk hydrate, hydraulic setting materials or synthetic dispersions and the lime render bulk together with colour giving pigments, and finally either sand or quartz dust. The chemical relationship with the render base is not in itself a critical factor, but it does however lead to a firm connexion (adhesion) with the fresh render base as long as this still has a certain amount of chemical activity. (The setting process of render mortars lasts, according to composition and thickness, under certain conditions up to two years.) Since render and paint demonstrate a chemical-alkaline reaction, mutual carbonization is possible; in this process a homogeneous uniformity forms between the render and paint.

Silicone pigments: silicone pigments are clear as glass binding agents which mainly consist of waterglass, free silicic acid and other materials which can form silicones. Like the special white and colour pigments which belong to this group, they combine themselves (by means of siliconization) indissolubly with the undersurface. Silicone paints are resistant to weathering, smoke gases and other chemical vapours. The paint film prevents the penetration of damp from the exterior without however preventing wall breathing. The undersurface must be firm, clean, dry and absorptive. (Thus engineering bricks are unsuitable for this.) Usually one major coat over an undercoat is sufficient. The undercoat must be allowed to dry out for at least 24 hours. In order to achieve a better with the base, the first coat should always be applied with powerful brush strokes. Only the second coat may, if necessary, be sprayed on. Even rolling on the second coat can be thoroughly recommended. Silicone paint should be applied generously, and well spread. It should always be applied wet on wet and working hand in hand. Unbroken areas should be painted without breaks. If it is absolutely necessary to make a break, then the point must be sharply delineated. There are more coloured paints available of this category than of lime paints. Since the silicone binding agents are particularly strong, pastel colours as well as rich and strong toned colours can be chosen. Apart from firmly stuck chalk, cement or silicone paints, all traces of old paints must be removed before applying fresh coats of silicone paints. It is never possible to remove the old traces of oil paints and dispersion paints, so that such a surface will always be unsuitable for silicone paints. Cement paints can be covered with silicone paint, but on the other hand, dispersion paint cannot.

Cement paints: cement paints are composed of factory produced mixes of white cement and hydrated lime. Numerous pastel colours are available as well as white. The mineral powder must be stirred in water and thinned down until suitable for applying: no further additives are necessary. These cement paints are weather- and water-resistant and water-repellent, although they are to a high degree permeable. By reason of their long-lasting alkaline content they do not become a breeding ground for fungi and bacteria. This paint requires an absorptive and gripping base so that a smooth dense base is inappropriate. The area must be cleaned of dust and dirt deposits. Irregular surfaces or those only slightly absorptive should be thoroughly pre-wetted. The necessary two or three coats should where possible be applied by brush and for the final coat one can also use a sheepskin roller. It is also possible to spray with a painter's spray or compressed air spray (nozzle opening 2.5 to 3 mm); however, the use of a paint brush is preferable. If such a combined painting technique is used, i.e. if the final coat is applied by spray, only paint which is still wet should be sprayed on. Awkward bases, as for example very absorbent bricks, should be painted with three coats by brush at intervals of 24 hours. The length of time that prepared paint is usable is 4 hours. Coverage for two coats is approximately 400 to 500 g/m² and for three coats 500 to 600 g/m². It should be possible to estimate exact figures, for example for big buildings, by means of a test area. The original tones can be mixed at will on the building so that one has a wide variety of available colours. Cement paint can be applied even in bright sunlight, but on the other hand it should not be used in heavy rain, bad fog, temperatures under 5° C, or if there is any likelihood of night frost. Cement paint is not affected by acid industrial waste gases. Cement paints are very alkaline (Ph value about 12). It is therefore not recommended that cement-based lime renders or cement paints should be subsequently treated with a colourless water-repellent protective coat (e.g. a sprayed coat of silicone preparations). Paints, on account of their workability and water-repellent effects, are superior to the once usual lime render of white cement, lime hydrate and quartz sand which was mixed on the site. Paints also provide adequate protection against downpours of rain.

Dispersion paints

There is hardly a single base to which dispersion paint cannot be applied. Furthermore, many types of surface effect are possible. Mineral paints have a matt, more or less coarse grained, surface. On the other hand, with dispersion paints one can vary between a matt, silky sheen to a high gloss surface. Fundamentally, however, it is a question of the paint binders which produce a cohesive film which is important for the purposes of protection. In a normal application with a matt, velvet like surface, a regular cohesive layer forms. Their weather-resistance has been proved. As far as the choice of colours is concerned there is in effect no limit.

Paint and the technique of application: those binding agents which are based on the raw materials p.v.a., p.v. proprionate, acrylic acid esters and their mixed polymerisates or on the mixed polymerisate dispersion styrol butadienes, produce elastic films which resist weak acids or alkalis. On new air-dried render no soap formation from the binding agents occurs. The dry films are porous and therefore permeable for water vapour and other gases.

In practice it is of no special importance whether the proportion of binding agent consists of one or more of the above-mentioned raw materials because (apart from the dispersed type of synthetic material or synthetic resin) there are no great differences from the point of view of application. All synthetic material dispersions are completely synthetic products which contain no naturally drying paint oil so that a new render base, which still reacts slightly alkaline, does

not necessarily have to be neutralized if the water dampness has dried out, by treatment with so-called "fluates" (silicous fluoric acid salts in a watery solution). Parts which have to be rendered later should in each case be "fluated" once or twice and post-washed. (Pay attention to the instructions!) For paint with dispersions on external rendered areas, the following fundamental rules are applicable: for durability, clarity of colour is necessary and for a uniform finish at long range an adequate layer consistency (dry film consistency) is necessary. Therefore the amount stated by the manufacturers of dispersion paints should not be reduced. For buildings in climatically very exposed areas (on the coastline, in mountains, or in an industrial area) even a third coat is recommended. Delivery categories: dispersion paints are delivered in the following varieties:

a) Non-pigmented dispersions with binding properties in which the choice and amount of colour (white and colour pigments) is left to the user and he himself makes up usable dispersion paints. The painting trade makes but little use of this possibility.

b) Non-pigmented thin flowing dispersions which are essentially used for colourless or slightly opaque primers (primer and consolidation agents) and for colourless protective and shiny coats to which, however, pigmented dispersion paints can also be added. Also, there are special agents for primers which bind diffusive soluble ferrous salts and which prevent undesirable brown marks appearing later in the dispersion paint.

c) Dispersion paints which are ready for use or in the form of a paste: the latter are prepared by the addition of water.

d) Dispersion paint renders: these are façade paints on a dispersion base with fine quartz or sand. They give an appearance similar to render. Like the paints mentioned in section (c) the "paint-render" can be delivered in white or light ivory. Shading off into other colours is achieved by means of adding coloured pastes.

e) Dispersion façade render or render fillers which serve to smooth out irregular patches. They are applied with renderer's tools (according to the product), are wetted after drying, and make good the irregularities. They are also suitable for remedying small faults in the render (nowadays they are almost always included under the heading "dispersion paints" as in section (c) or they are painted with dispersion paint renders. It is worth mentioning that the paints in the individual groups can be mixed one with another. So one can make use of them according to the desired surface finish: smooth, slightly plastic, fine to coarse grain, and so on. This characteristic can not always be deduced from the instructions. Often it is only possible to establish this on the site by painting sample areas. The renders and fillers mentioned in sections d) and e) above are also suitable for the bedding in of glass fibre thread or synthetic materials (perlon or nylon) since the necessity of covering shrinkage cracks in the top render has frequently occurred. Meanwhile dispersion paint masses have also been developed which are intended to eliminate the use of glass fibre thread as these paints are able to make an elastic bridge over the cracks.

The masonry breathing of dispersion paints: the question suggests itself as to whether the masonry breathing is adequately guaranteed in layers which are of a similar nature to render. In a communal research programme with the Lime

Industry Union, dispersion paint manufacturers today have so adjusted their products that in spite of the film formation which does occur in the use of synthetic dispersions it is nevertheless possible to allow the render and the masonry beneath it to breathe. In the types mentioned above, although very different, this breathing is regulated either by the thickness of the dry film of paint or by the additives – e.g. in the form of fine sand (quartz mores).

The question of a smooth or raw surface should not only be considered from the aesthetic and economic points of view. Certainly one would choose a smoother surface in areas where there is a considerable amount of soot in order to preclude the danger of dirt and dust deposits. But often, one is also forced to apply rougher coats because the skin of render has irregularities which cannot be covered by the so-called smooth paint as the coat of paint follows the irregularities. To avoid hollows and bumps which frequently become visible in rendering on account of obscuration of the surface which takes place where scaffold poles overlap, one increasingly uses the most appropiate paint or façade renders which in effect produce a third layer of render.

The timing of applications of dispersion paints externally: it is inexpedient to paint an area with dispersion paints straight from the rendering scaffolding just a few hours or days after the final application of render, because under certain circumstances the paints could retard the setting process of the mortar. This is especially true in the case of renders of mortar group Ia, i.e. for mortars which are mixed with air lime. Mortar of group Ib together with water limes or lime cement mortar and high hydraulic mortar of group II can be painted earlier if the mortar reaches a compressive strength of at least 10 kg/cm² after 28 days and air finishing. For all kinds of render and all dispersion paints it has been proved however that there is a waiting period of six to eight weeks. The render paint base and its preparation: the principle that the paint base must be firmer than the coat applied to it ever can be is also applicable to dispersion paints. Brittle and rippling renders are fundamentally unsuitable for painting. By means of twice applying fluates, a surface strength is achieved by the formation of calcium silicate if alkalinity is still present. Recently, priming agents have been developed on a synthetic resin base which, on account of their good filling effect, are equally suitable as an agent for making the render firm. In unclear cases, in order to avoid all risks, the manufacturer of the chosen dispersion paint material should be brought in so that the render can be tested before the instructions are written up. As already mentioned, it is now only necessary to apply "fluates" to renovated areas which have a stronger alkalinity than the remainder of the surface. Obviously an application of "fluates" is appropriate to balance differing absorption effects of a rendered area. An application of "fluates" is then under the circumstances damaging because apart from the narrowing of the pores (which does not harm the breathing of the render) a prophylactic protection against the growth of fungi has been arrived at.

Covering paints and colourless applications: apart from any priming which might perhaps be necessary, two coats are generally required.

As desired, the first coat can be paint render or a similar sand-containing dispersion paint, whilst the top coat should be applied in the chosen colour. To achieve a smooth, regular

ground for painting, façade render, render filler, or such materials can be applied with a spatula between the primer and the final coat. On plinth areas, undersides of gables or for water-proofing on the weather sides, semi-gloss coats with colourless dispersions are appropriate. Agents of this kind are also in use as so-called stone protection agents. They preclude the disintegration caused by aggressive chemicals (smoke gases, etc.).

Renders of coloured mortars

Paint on render forms only a thin film which can be mechanically easily harmed or destroyed. Its permanence depends on whether a firm connexion (lasting adhesion) can be preserved with the render as a base. On the other hand render of coloured mortar is less likely to be damaged. As long as it is not destroyed through to the base coat of render, its appearance suffers little. The colour here is not an element separated from the construction. The two are preserved together and the colour requires no special protective measures. If the mortar is efficiently worked, such a render will have a long life in colour effect but has the disadvantage that it is expensive to renew or repair.

The colour effect is also not exactly the same as that of the render paints, which are available in almost any colour. With a render of coloured mortars, an the other hand, the impression of the material is preserved on account of the limited choice of pigment and of the limited pigment additive to the mortar even when, as nowadays, pigments in coloured mortars make it possible to achieve particularly strong tones. Façade renders of coloured mortar can be divided into two groups: those produced in cement works and those which are coloured on the site. The dry mortars prepared in the works (the so-called "noble" renders) can be made available to any specification in the most varied of grain sizes and colour tones, and ready to use.

The difficulty of producing coloured mortars on the site lies in the fact that the mix must be made up the same way each time. Even the slightest difference in composition would show in the colour. Since for one wall area several mixes are always needed, success will depend on each load turning out the same colour as the others. It must not only be guaranteed that the proportion of binding agent to sand and of binding agent to pigment remains the same, but also that the sand never varies in its grain composition nor in its purity. Therefore it is recommended to store up the necessary amounts of raw material for all the render before work begins.

Choice of white and coloured pigments

Coloured renders should only contain pigments which are light-fast and are either lime-proof or cement-proof. Such pigments must not be discoloured or destroyed by the binding agents or the additives. Cement-proof pigments are also lime-proof. In dubious cases a simple investigation is possible (although the pigment manufacturer usually gives adequate information concerning the properties).

To test the alkaline proofness, a sample of the dry pigment is taken and is mixed with lime in a clean container. The mixture is then covered and left to stand overnight. The next day another sample is mixed in the same way. It is then possible to compare the colours of both samples. Pigments which will be exposed to considerable stress, e.g. in respect of weather resistance, must nevertheless retain their colour; the lime water lying above the pigments should not be coloured. If there is some colouring present in the water, the pigment contains water soluble colouring (mostly to improve the tone of colour) and is therefore unsuitable.

To test cement proofness, standard cement is mixed with and without pigment in water and is spread out, like a cake, on a pane of glass. After one day the samples are placed in water and are left there for six days after which they are air dried. The "cakes" must not have changed in colour after drying by comparison with those not immersed, nor must they show any efflorescence. If efflorescence is present, it should be ascertained whether the non-coloured cement "cake" does not also suffer from efflorescence.

The most important pigments for lime and cement mortars:

Colour tone	Usual trade name
White	Lithopone
	Titanium white
	Titanium dioxide Rutil
Yellow	Naples yellow
	Nickel titanium yellow
	Iron oxide yellow
	Yellow ochre
	Terra di Siena (unburnt)
Red	Iron oxide red
	Red ochre
	Iron red
	Ultramarine red, cement-proof
Brown	Iron oxide brown
	Burnt ochre
	Umber, manganese brown
Green	Chrome oxide green
	Chrome oxide hydrate green
	Ultramarine green, cement-proof
Blue	Ultramarine blue, cement-proof
	Light blue
Black	Iron oxide black
	Cement black
	Lamp black
	Grape black

(The table is not complete. For special purposes, as for example painting render and for graffito work, further pigments are available.)

Pigments are an extremely fine powder which has a large surface; in mortar, they take on the function which the finest sand would have. Consequently they can only be added in amounts which would not require additional binding agents in order to bind all the constituents of the mortar firmly together. A rule of thumb for practical work on the site is that the pigment should not exceed five per cent of the binding content so that the normal properties of a firm mortar can be achieved. Experience has taught us that one can only choose those pigments which yield the desired colour when the smallest amounts are added. Synthetic iron oxide pigments are superior to natural iron oxides in their colouring ability because they do not show any wastage. The colours in naturally produced pigments – ochres, umbers, iron reds and so on – reduce, as is well known, the colouring ability, apart from the fact that types rich in colour require a greater amount of binding agent.

Noble renders from coloured mortars

For coloured dry mortars manufactured in the works (called "noble" renders) only selected basic constituents can be used, above all only those sand grains which have previously been carefully cleaned and are collected together in carefully limited grain groups, so that the same grain composition occurs. In the works there are also very reliable mixing machines available which give an optimum mix such as is never possible on the site. Consequently, noble render is superior to any other coloured mortar.

No further additive should be mixed in with the noble renders on the site because it could lead to chemical reactions with the mortar constituents, especially with the pigment, a process which could result in discolouring or spots in the render. There are also noble renders with water-repellent properties, so there is no need to add proofing agents. To ensure that the render really achieves the desired colour, tap water only should be used to make up the mortar.

A further advantage in using noble renders is that the most appropriate method of rendering can be chosen. Thus the special conditions prevailing where the building is being erected can be considered, above all the rate of air pollution. Noble renders are available as scratch render, spray render, trowel-thrown render, trowelled render, and plate-smoothed render. For the plinth, stone and washed renders are suitable. According to the size of sand grain, finer or rougher surfaces can be achieved. Through the addition of certain stones, as for example limespar, such rendered surfaces give a very lively effect. A special means of giving form to coloured mortars is the graffito effect.

G External walls in exposed concrete

Concrete fabrication and shuttering technique

Technically, exposed concrete must fulfil the same conditions as normal concrete, but additional requirements have to be observed in its production, regarding the composition of the mix, the choice of aggregate as well as the preparation, batching and yield in order to achieve a uniform face in structure and colour:

1. The architect must in the first place establish the kind of formwork to correspond with the desired effect. Technical expediency must be properly considered. It is most important that the formwork should be well braced and lined up.

2. A careful examination of the binding agent, of the aggregate and of the water should always precede the production of concrete.

The composition of the concrete mix can be discovered by means of personal tests and sample batches. Shrinkage cracks and irregular colouring (streaking or cloudiness) can be traced back to the inadequate structure of the concrete.

3. All binding agents and aggregates must be kept ready in sufficient amounts for the whole building right from the very start, in order to eliminate differences between various deliveries.

4. It is necessary to plan in sufficient joints because exposed concrete must contain a high proportion of cement (at least 300 kg/m³) for adequate weather resistance. It is therefore more inclined than normal concrete to shrink.

5. It is possible to use appropriate cement which is less susceptible to shrinkage, in concrete. Cements which can retain water for a long time have proved themselves in general to be better than those which only keep the water for a short time, because the repelled water can rise on the internal face of the formwork and leave behind, on smooth concrete, unattractive stripes.

6. Aggregates should always be gauged by weight. The largest grade depends on the arrangement of the reinforcement as well as on the appropriate maximum sieve size of the total aggregate. The portion of fines under 0·2 mm is especially important in exposed concrete. The necessary washed aggregate for exposed concrete seldom has this portion of fines; it must therefore be added separately. The size of grain is also dependent on the form of the building. Strong, simple outlines permit coarse grades, whilst broken façades require a less coarse grade.

7. With additives there should be careful testing in advance to see whether they cause any damaging side effects. They must also be added equally to the entire concrete because they can alter its colour and thus cause unequal surface effects. In processes to retard setting, water-absorbent formwork should not be used, as it would draw water irregularly, over a longer period, from the concrete.

8. The concrete mix should be so prepared that the concrete is uniformly dense and is low in air pockets. Concrete which has been made up too stiffly without an adequate addition of fines can only be equally consolidated with difficulty, even with vibrators. Concrete which is too soft can easily segregate. In either case the result is an uneven surface.

9. The external covering of the reinforcement must be at least 1½ times the size of the largest stone. If concrete is to be processed later on (bush-hammered, for example), then from the very outset the depth of surface treatment should be considered and the cover to the reinforcement taken into account. There are various synthetic non-rusting shuttering bolts: under all circumstances they should be exactly positioned according to an accurate drawing. The resulting holes should later be carefully filled. Starters should be grout-painted during the concreting process. Binding wires and clamps should be positioned within the reinforcement and not the reinforcement cover area.

10. So that the construction joints do not stand out later, the consolidation of the concrete (vibrating) must be carried out very thoroughly.

After-treatment of external exposed concrete

When the work is finished the wall areas are cleaned of formwork oil residue and all spillages (e.g. deposits of cement dust). Some types of concrete, if they have a dense structure and slight capillaries, can even be sufficiently weather-proof without any additional measures. In domestic building, however, it is usually necessary to improve the technical qualities of the concrete by means of additives or paints incorporating water-resistant agents. Such coatings produce a film-like effect – e.g. in the use of lacquers, synthetic emulsions and dispersion paints, all of which offer good protection against damp. But even then they can only be effective if the total wall face is uniformly treated. Hints which would be of universal value cannot be given on account of the large number of such agents on the market. Generally such treatments have to be renewed every five years.

Lightweight concrete usually requires an additional external protective layer in order to be resistant to the weather. Instead of the relatively expensive normal render one can choose quick-drying, synthetic, spatula-applied materials, or paint renders, for these rather smooth surfaces.

Colourings of exposed concrete

In the course of time even natural grey exposed concrete undergoes certain colour changes. If one wants to colour the exposed concrete, there are the following possibilities:

1. Coloured natural stones as aggregates: all weather-resistant stones are suitable, i.e. those which have no organic clay or other unsuitable admixtures.

2. Coloured stone and crushed sands: instead of the colours of the aggregate, the concrete can be permanently coloured by means of the fines; however, the mixing proportions of the concrete (fines content) must be retained. A greater proportion of fines would require more cement; it would also increase the risk of shrinkage. Coloured sands must be just as clean as the larger grades.

3. Coloured binding agent: by using certain cements, many shades of colour from grey to white can be achieved. White exposed concrete can also be manufactured to the desired quality.

4. Cement colours: admixtures of cement colours produce natural tones which do not jar. However, they make production more difficult and more expensive. These basic colours could be considered: red, black, brown, white and yellow; more rarely, blue and green. The colour pigments, which must be cement-fast, that is alkaline-proof, light-proof and weather-resistant, can either be mixed into the cement itself or be added during the later concrete mixing process. On site, the first process is preferable. After concreting, the cement skin should be removed.

5. Painting onto exposed concrete: only cement-fast colour pigments may be used because cement could, as an alkaline substance, produce reactions with certain coloured pigments, which would alter the tone. In addition, the pigments must be light-fast. Likewise, only weather-resistant colouring agents should be used. Weather resistance is generally dependent on the binding agent. (The manufacturer's stated mixing proportions of binding agents to pigments should be strictly adhered to.)

Prefabricated reinforced concrete elements

Prefabricated parts of reinforced concrete can be used on external walls as infill panels for system building and for curtain walls. Similarly, when claddings are of precast concrete with exposed aggregate, one part of the job can be dealt with in the factory rather than on the site because the job can be carried out far more rationally in the works by using assembly line processes.

If not only one part of the wall but the wall itself – inclusive of external skin, inner cladding and the necessary windows and doors – is all prefabricated in the factory, one has arrived at assembly wall units which fulfil all stability, thermal insulating and physical building functions. On the site, the elements are just linked one with another and with other parts of the building.

With the change in processing, a series of technical, economical and manufacturing questions have arisen. The following comments are however only intended to outline briefly the fundamental principles of the form and execution of assembly buildings which are of importance for external walls. The climate of inhabited rooms is decisively influenced by the materials used to make up the external wall panels. Concrete, above all heavy concrete with a dense structure, has a high thermal conductivity figure and a relatively slight thermal expansion coefficient. Furthermore it has a very high damp diffusion resistance factor. On the basis of these properties concrete as the sole constructional material is unsuitable for the external walls of inhabited rooms; it requires additional thermal insulation.

Therefore multi-layer panels are used almost exclusively for prefabricated external wall units. The external concrete layer is then a part of the wall construction which has also, together with thermal protection, to fulfil stability and thermal retention functions. But then from the constructional point of view the thermal retention layer is badly positioned. As a rule, then, wall elements consist of three layers: the external concrete layer gives weather protection for which it is well suited on account of its hardness and waterproofness. Apart from a simple exposed concrete with a coat of paint, or washed concrete, certain other materials, are suitable for an external skin, including split tiles, ceramic tiles, and medium size mosaic. Behind the external skin lies the thermal retention layer usually of rigid foam materials. Some processes also use glass or mineral wool mats, Leca (expanded clay) or aerated concrete. This inner layer, intended to provide thermal protection, is placed as near as possible to the exterior; a third layer takes over the stability function, a core of heavy concrete. In some processes the internal face has a coat of plaster. The external concrete skin is linked with the internal one by means of concrete fillets, steel anchors, or by links of reinforcement. In certain systems the windows, painted and glazed, are inserted in the works. Large external wall components are also frequently produced in so-called "mixed process" on the site together with ceilings and internal walls. For it is exactly at this point in the building process – if it is well done – that there are considerable advantages in prefabrication, on account of the high production costs of a traditional system.

But in all these wall systems particular attention must be paid to damp diffusion and the possibly associated dew formation on and in the wall construction. So it is strongly recommended that diffusion should always be investigated either by calculations or by drawings. Even in a careful construction it is not possible to avoid thermal bridges. The actual thermal retention of such a sandwich panel often only makes a difference of two-thirds of the value which has been calculated. The joints between the individual slabs must be able, without obstruction, to take up differences in settlement and distortion in the external wall panels, which occur as a result of temperature tensions, shrinking of the concrete, movement of the body of the building because of settlement or wind forces. Furthermore the measurement differences of the individual elements must be taken up.

The economics of a construction are largely determined by the planning: this is especially true of system building. Fundamentally there are two possible ways: either one first develops, on the basis of a constructional process, the spatial unit and then determines the size and form of the elements, or one uses assembly constructional systems from which a ground plan can be worked out at will using various, previously decided, elements. The designer generally takes as his basis a more or less large grid. A small grid can be suitably adjusted to various domestic requirements. The smaller the elements are, the more suitable they are for buildings of various forms and consequently one can reduce the number of types necessary for any particular building. But the processes immediately become more expensive the more varied are the types of element incorporated. A consequence of this is that there are far more joints which not only complicate the building process but also send up the cost of the process because of the labour required. On the other hand, a large grid can easily lead to rigid ground plans and uneconomical dimensions without the value of the unit being correspondingly increased. A large grid system, however, is advantageous from the point of view of manufacture, transport and assembly.

To summarize: the economic advantage of the prefabrication factory increases with the size of the elements; simultaneously the labour costs in assembly decrease because of the smaller number of joints to be made and on account of its being simpler to adjust. The optimum size of the prefabricated elements is, however, limited by the manufacturer's own economic criteria and transport regulations.

H External walls with exposed aggregate / face textured precast concrete panels

Concrete blocks include all goods produced in a concrete works and hardened on the site, and which consist of reinforced or unreinforced cement concrete. The following products also belong to this group: concrete products (with untreated exposed surface), exposed aggregate concrete panels (with treated exposed surface), and reinforced concrete prefabricated components (for system building).

There are the same prerequisites for the surface treatment of concrete products as for *in situ* exposed concrete.

The material

The increase in efficiency in concrete production (e.g. ready-to-use concrete of 600 Kp/cm²) and the use of high tensile steel (with prefabricated elements of 2·4 and 2·8 Kp/cm²) have made possible considerable further development in concrete, reinforced concrete and prestressed concrete. This development, together with new machines for the manufacture, distribution and general handling of concrete, furthered the use of prefabricated building elements and also led to the increasing use of precast, exposed face panels for external walls.

Precast textured face panels can be produced in almost any size – from the small element to the one-storey high element the size of a room – and provide innumerable possibilities for the structural form and colouring of the surface. Such elements can thus be used for many purposes and shapes. Their efficiency properties are also variable to a certain degree.

Usually, textured face panels are manufactured in double layers. Their core consists of normal or reinforced concrete whilst the facing contains the desired composition of natural stone aggregates. Both concretes must, according to their technical properties, harmonize well one with another and be inseparably linked. The higher labour costs for the two processes are, by comparison with homogeneous concrete, more than compensated for by economies in the material. There are also concrete slabs which (like textured natural stone) are cut out of a homogeneous block.

The surface is simultaneously decided upon when the formwork is chosen:

a) Smooth surfaces: they can in themselves occur in various colours or be coloured afterwards (mono-coloured, variously coloured, or multi-coloured surfaces).

b) Treated surfaces: by means of washing, sanding, stonemason's work, polishing.

c) Patterned surfaces: by inserting designed panels, e.g. alternating rough and smooth surfaces. The size, form and direction of panels are chosen according to the desired effect. The joints can be staggered or lined up.

d) Profiled surfaces: by inserting fillets, etc.

e) Surfaces formed by a sculptor: by inserting plaster of paris shapes, clay or synthetic material, or by later working – e.g. sandblasting.

f) The broken surface: open or glazed apertures.

In each case the exposed face of the precast textured panels contains natural, mostly coloured, stone aggregates in natural grey, white or coloured cement bed. One can use stones of almost any kind for this; even a marble appearance is possible. For marble concrete (not to be confused with artificial marble of plaster of paris, anhydrate, etc.) one uses for example grains and dust from polishable stones, particularly marble and serpentine. By means of the corresponding basic ingredients (for example granite, basalt or porphyry) numerous colourings can be achieved.

In contrast to exposed concrete the precast textured panel is characterized by the fact that after the formwork has been struck and the surface has been treated, the grey cement skin disappears and aggregate and colour come to the surface. To achieve this there are the following procedures:

a) To decorrode, brush off and de-acidify (washed concrete): to simplify work on the site, setting retarders are put on the inside of the formwork before concreting takes place.

b) Sanding: the concrete is sand-blasted.

c) Stonemason's treatment: by this means the visual colour

effect and the contrast between the various stones and the background is strengthened. One treats concrete textured panels in the same way as natural stones (chiselling, bush-hammering and punching, etc.). But whilst natural stone, by its very nature, requires certain processes which themselves influence the finished shape, precast concrete panels are in their final form the moment they leave the formwork; they only require a texture. Certainly one can imitate natural stones in precast concrete slabs, which in any case (as for example sandstones and conglomerate) have a similar texture to concrete. This can sometimes be necessary when historical buildings are being renovated. However, in normal building of high blocks one should limit the form to the colour which is appropriate to the precast concrete textured slabs.

d) Polishing: one can smooth all natural stones and polish some of them. By this means the mineral texture of the slabs is cut up. The smoothed and rubbed area can be more or less fine. To achieve special effects it is also possible to put split stones into the formwork and the area which is later to be smoothed.

Handling and placing of precast textured concrete slabs

The precast textured concrete slabs serve various purposes; the method of production is correspondingly variable. Thus, constructional elements, external wall slabs, or screen walls (tracery and filigree-like open walls) are possible.

As constructional elements, precast textured concrete slabs are processed, like natural stones, in combination with the backing wall. But there are also hollow precast textured concrete slabs which are filled with *in situ* concrete. However, they can only be used in buildings which require no thermal retention. In the main, precast textured concrete slabs are used as external wall slabs. Form, dimensions, aggregate (colour and treatment) can be ordered as desired or from a series out of the catalogue.

The slabs must be frost-resistant, waterproof, colour-fast and accurate in size. They are produced, where possible, with thin walls so they can be transported by hand: if two men are to handle a slab it must not be larger than 0·50–0·75 m² if it is 4 to 6 cm thick. Larger slabs also require reinforcement. This, yet again, would necessitate a thicker slab in order to ensure sufficient cover to the reinforcement.

The wall slabs are either applied directly to the walls or with an air gap. In the first process the slabs must be fully mortared on the back face and jointed, which is especially necessary with smaller slabs. There is some divergence of opinion about the appropriate width of joints. So that they can be well pointed, they should not be too narrow (at least 6 mm, preferably 8 to 10 mm wide). Even when the mortar filling is applied in a relatively fluid form it is hardly possible to avoid air pockets. Altogether, the same problems, especially physical-constructional problems, occur in this process as in the laying of slabs of natural stone or tiles: the cladding must prevent the penetration of downpours of rain, but at the same time must permit the diffusion of water vapour from the interior. At the same time condensation, which could be damaging, must not be allowed to form within the wall construction. With concrete slabs there are also the influences from the shrinkage and creeping of the concrete and from the longitudinal changes in the slabs in temperature variations. So it is advisable to apply the slabs with back ventilation and with flexible joints (open joints with corresponding profiles or closed joints with a permanent mastic). Then the slab expansion, which can be considerable, according to the permanence and intensity of the sunshine and the absorptive ability of the coloured surface, is limited to the individual slab. Just like traditional claddings for weather protection – hung tiles, slate, or roofing stone slabs – the slabs can also be hung in front of the wall with overlapping joints. Such wall slabs are manufactured in series, for example out of very rich special concrete. On their exposed face they have a permanently multi-coloured sintered sand coating about 50 x 25 cm large and at the most 3 cm thick. On all sides there are overlapping joints and they can thus be set both horizontally and vertically on to mortar strips. Each slab is fixed once more. The air between the slab and the wall is connected to the external air by means of the open overlapping joints.

The back ventilated cladding guarantees that damp which penetrates through the external skin evaporates in the aired void without reaching the internal skin. At the same time it ensures that water vapour penetrating from the interior behind the weatherproof external skin can be led off to the exterior by means of openings. Small slabs with a peripheral length of 40 to 60 cm can be set on mortar strips. In each case they should be additionally connected with the wall by means of appropriate fastenings (cramps, hooks or anchors); larger slabs are only anchored in this way.

In general the same hints for fixing are valid as for natural stone (see walls, in natural stone, page above). However, in precast textured slabs the anchors can be concreted in the works at the same time as the element is being manufactured. The fixings must be protected against rust (where possible, stainless steel). Gypsum should not be used. If the slabs are set on to mortar strips, then the surface to be clad should be carefully tested and eventually prepared in order to guarantee a perfect adhesion. If the surface is very absorbent it may be necessary to whitewash the wall first or to coat it with coarse-grained mortar rich in cement because otherwise the water which is needed for setting would be too quickly drawn off. On walls which take up no, or very little, water a spray coating of cement mortar is absolutely imperative. Precast textured concrete slabs are also very suitable as a cladding for walls of *in situ* concrete (the so-called "mantelbeton") whereby the slabs can serve in the concreting process as permanent shuttering.

In place of the core of the precast textured concrete slab of densely consolidated concrete, it is possible to place a thermal retention layer behind the facing (for example gas concrete expanded clay or pumice). As the external layer must have a dense structure to provide the necessary weather protection, the inner wall damp of the *in situ* concrete which is created during manufacture can only escape to the interior. In an attempt to avoid these difficulties, ventilation tubes have often been placed within the slab in front of the retention layer.

"Mantelbeton" with permanent shuttering of precast textured concrete slabs is, however, also sensitive to temperature. When the external concrete layer is warmed, a warmth vapour results between this and the retention layer because the heat cannot flow to the interior. Furthermore, since the cladding

and wall concrete were manufactured at different times, stresses result because the *in situ* concrete works, shrinks and creeps more than the facing slab which is already hardened when it is built in.

With prefabricated multi-layered concrete components, as used in system building, or if façade cladding has back ventilation, it is possible to avoid these difficulties. Obviously, it is not possible to use the slabs as permanent shuttering. But, to compensate, one creates clearer technical and physical relationships.

I External walls with asbestos cement elements

Permanent colouring, slabs of large area and light in weight are the chief characteristics of asbestos cement material. Thus, asbestos cement panels, in various sizes and colours, are primarily used for curtain walls and external walls with back ventilation. They provide permanent weather protection, increase the thermal retention, and require no further maintenance. Again, asbestos cement is heat-resistant, non-inflammable, resistant to violent temperature changes, frost-resistant, corrosion-resistant and rot-proof. Coloured asbestos cement panels are processed in combination with modern thermal materials into components and often appear in the construction of light external walls as panelling in the bearing frame.

The material

Asbestos cement panels consist of a mixture of asbestos fibres and cement in which the tensile asbestos threads, masticised with cement, form a "reinforcement" to the cement base. After a special disintegrating process the asbestos threads are enveloped in cement slurry, taken up into a sieve cylinder, straightened out and processed via an endless felt belt into a thin asbestos cement mat which is transformed, layer by layer, to the desired thickness, on to a forming roller. At the same time, superfluous binding water is withdrawn. The damp asbestos cement layer is cut up and unwound from the roller as a non-hardened malleable slab (Hatschek process). Flat panels are then usually subjected to high pressure before being further hardened, whilst at the same time further binding water is withdrawn from the fresh slab. Such slabs are characterized by their increased firmness.

Asbestos cement is a homogeneous building material and by reason of its cement content is comparable with concrete; it must be subjected to a hardening process of 28 days followed by further curing. For compressive, tensile, and thus also bending, strength, together with the type and efficiency of the cement, the size of the asbestos threads and their arrangement are decisive. The water absorptive ability and associated frost-resistance are dependent on the density of the surface as well as on structure and porosity. Water vapour diffusionability is likewise determined by these influences.

The modulus of elasticity, thermal expansion coefficients and thermal conductivity figure are, on account of the composition of asbestos cement, comparable with the values for concrete.

In the following table, those stabilities of asbestos cement which are appropriate in this context are contrasted with those of timber, steel and concrete:

Eternit Concrete Steel Softwood (quality class)

		Eternit [1]
Compressive strength (in direction of fibre) in Kp/cm²	D Breaking point D zul (?)	500—650 150—200
Tensile strength (in direction of fibre)	D Breaking point D zul (?)	100—180 30— 60
Bending strength	D Breaking point D zul (?)	170—260 60— 85

* The given figures relate to asbestos cement of the Eternit brand and are dependent on the properties of the cements used and asbestos fibres, as well as on the mix proportion and after-treatment. — 1) The permissible strength values are calculated on the assumption of a threefold factor of safety. — 2) The strength values for concrete were compared on the assumption of a cube strength W 28 = 300 Kp/cm². — 3) The breakage strength is subjected to many influences. The given values are approximate values which could be up to 40 per cent less in extreme cases.

Building materials which, when cement is being used, are produced as binding agents are inclined to shrink or creep according to the cement content and graining. Over a longer period these phenomena attenuate and fade away. They are influenced by the damp content and the water absorption ability and are subjected to changes of form as a result of temperature. To shorten this ageing process, the colour-treated asbestos cement products above all are steam-hardened, at the first stage of their hardening, in an autoclave under high temperatures and pressure. The tendency to shrink is thus almost completely removed. The composition of the raw materials is thus modified and adjusted to the mechanical-technical processes of steam-hardening.

Corrugated sheets of asbestos cement and special profiles in their well-known natural grey colour have been frequently used for many years as external walls of industrial buildings. Since the material can be easily shaped in its non-hardened condition, various special profiles have also been developed (e.g. coffered slabs) for the cladding of external walls.

Nowadays, asbestos cement panels for external walls are produced in numerous colours. The Eternit programme embraces, for example:

a) Single-coloured Eternit Colorit façade panels 4 mm thick of flat high-pressured panels with an inorganic colour coating which combines well with its base by reason of its composition.

b) Granulated Eternit Colorit façade slabs 4 mm thick, high-pressured and steam-hardened (strewn with ceramic granules).

c) Eternit Glasal panels 3·2, 6 and 8 mm thick. The raw slab consists of a mixture appropriate to the total process which is steam-hardened, after the usual manufacture, at the stage of beginning to harden. To these raw materials are added a special inorganic colour coating which in further special processes undergoes a siliconing with the base so that permanent weather-resistant, scratch-proof, and insoluble surfaces result. These panels are frequently described as enamelled cement panels on account of their internal colour layers.

d) Recently, white, through-coloured flat panels have been produced, up to 20 mm thick, for the cladding of external walls. These panels are also high-pressured and steam-hardened.

Of the above-named building materials Glasal panels, with steam-hardened flat panels, have been processed into spandrel and external wall elements. In using these, special building requirements regarding fire-resistance have to be considered. As asbestos cement panels cannot fulfil these requirements because of their thinness, the "asbestolux" fire protective slab was developed; this is especially suited to the manufacture of fire-resistant components; this is especially suited to the manufacture of fire-resistant components. Asbestolux panels contain special additives in their composition which have only a slight cubic weight. They are likewise steam-hardened.

External wall claddings with asbestos cement elements

In back-ventilated external wall claddings the external skin is by intention separated from the bearing external wall in order to eliminate the effects of damp in the airstream by means of this back ventilation and to guarantee a permanently dry atmosphere; consequently the thermal retention of the masonry is maintained. When Eternit elements are used, such back ventilation is achieved by means of various arrangements of the panels and subframes. One very common and economic method is to deploy the elements on a timber substructure. This enables any unevennesses of the bearing walls to be overcome by means of many fillets (counterbattens) so that the resulting cladding is well-aligned. There is the further possibility, if the building is a monolithic reinforced concrete structure, that an additional synthetic resin bonded mineral wool mat can be incorporated in the external wall of the roughly finished building. The vertical joints are covered with a special seal; horizontal joints are lapped. As far as the permanence of the timber substructure is concerned, the existing back ventilation, according to experience gained so far, is quite adequate for the full drying out of the timber slats. Moreover they are impregnated against these influences.

In many buildings the timber substructure is nowadays replaced by an asbestos cement substructure (flat panel strips 80 mm wide and 10 mm thick, with special adjustable spacers which are well aligned in the void in front of the wall). With this system it is possible to compensate for even the smallest unevennesses of the structural wall. The panels are screwed on in a similar way to the timber substructure. In order to collect information on the permanency of glues, in some cases panels are stuck with two-component glues instead of being screwed.

Nailing or screwing panels has, in certain cases, spoilt the surface of the asbestos. The visible fixing points can however be disguised by means of synthetic layered colour-matched covers. In the case of thicker panels it is possible for them to be fixed from the rear on to a light metal substructure by letting in special metal dowels. The thick, coloured Eternit panels already described are specially suitable for such a method, but thicker Glasal panels which can be glued to a naturally-coloured steam-hardened flat panel are also suitable.

External walls out of asbestos cement compound elements

In an attempt to rationalise construction, increasing use is made of compound panels to fill in skeleton frames. Such compound panels of asbestos cement are inserted as spandrel or external wall components. These lightweight constructions, together with their accessories and joints, must fulfil the basic requirements for external walls.

Usually asbestos cement compound slabs consist of Glasal panels on their external face. For the internal face, panels of the same thickness, a natural colour and steam-hardened, are used. Between these there is an appropriate insulating material consisting of synthetic foams, but also of foamed glass and other thermal insulating materials which can be stuck to the asbestos cement panels. A damp barrier is imperative for such an arrangement. The elements are produced on a conveyor belt to dimensions of 1·2 x 2·5 m and are characterised by their light weight, their weather-resistance, and high thermal retention. Noise insulation of monocoque compound elements is dependent, amongst other things, on the superficial weight of this part of the building. On this basis, there is a sound insulation for these compound elements and also for all other light elements; dependent on size, the sound insulation figure is about 35 dB. This value appears to be quite adequate for external walls, as opposed to party walls and ceilings, because for external walls sound insulation is ultimately dependent on the value of the window areas, usually a lower rating.

Prefabrication of asbestos cement panels

In the rationalization and prefabrication processes the question frequently arises as to how far it is possible to apply the external wall cladding at the manufacturing stage, when exceptionally large solid panel elements are to be used. Various processes for doing this are known. By virtue of their properties it would also be conceivable that coloured asbestos cement panels could be used in such a way, even though it would be necessary to solve various building and production problems. Furthermore, this question occurs in the production of buildings which are erected in *in situ* concrete (sliding formwork, "mantelbeton" and insulating formwork). Even here there would be a number of difficulties to be overcome, as indeed with all manufactured panel-shaped external wall claddings, before practicable processes with asbestos cement material could be recommended.

J External walls in timber

There are certain fundamental rules for the appropriate use of timber on the exterior of buildings, which are necessary for an architecturally satisfying and constructionally adequate solution. If they are followed, later defects, which can be expensive and require constant repairs, will be eliminated.
a) Timber, on account of its colour and structure, has a warm and lively effect and is best used in areas which will be used by people. Although it has virtually lost its earlier importance as a structural material in the building, it now offers a wider field of application, especially as cladding and

panelling and particularly as a design element with its own visual attraction.
b) Timber infill should always suit the structure of the building. It would be quite wrong in a building of today to aim at woodwork effects such as one finds for example in old country houses.
c) The natural ageing of the timber (weathering and discolouring) must be foreseen at the planning stage not only from the constructional point of view but also from the angle of later visual impression. Untreated firs, for example, become silver-grey after a very short time in timber stores in the mountains, whereas in coastal stores they turn dark grey. To attempt at any cost to preserve the fresh condition of the timber with its colour and graining would not be true to the material, quite apart from the fact that the ageing process in timber cannot be held up by any precautions whatsoever.
d) The characteristics of the material, the effects of weathering, and the changes in a material which is a living thing, must be considered from the outset in the construction. Arrangements for regular care should be made.
e) A good knowledge of the properties and characteristics of the various types of timber is necessary for the right choice of timber from the point of view of a suitable visual effect as well as an appropriate constructional process and a thorough treatment of the surface. This is especially true for the numerous exotic woods which are today being used for building.
f) Surface treatment of timber is very varied today primarily because aggressive atmospheric conditions have to be contended with. In addition, each type of wood requires different treatment and materials: what in one case is successful can in another lead to deleterious effects. One should always seek advice from a well versed specialist. If the right species of wood is chosen, if the construction is appropriate to requirements and properly carried out and if the timber is thoroughly treated and constantly maintained, then timber can, by comparison with other external wall claddings, be equally suitable or even superior.

Bearing frames and walls in timber

The use of timber for buildings constantly occupied by human beings has been considerably curtailed on account of its ready inflammability. Since buildings are increasingly prefabricated, timber and timber products are, however, used more and more for external walls by virtue of their good properties and their workability. Prefabricated processes (machine, industrial processes and quality-improving pre-treatment and drying out) can be used to advantage for timber. As prefabricated timber elements are light in weight and have a high shear and bending strength they can be easily transported. With the exception of timber products (chipboard, etc.) which have to be clad, they are not usually monolithic constructions, but timber panel and frame elements which are clad with timber either in the factory or on the site. Thus to some extent the same stipulations are valid here as for wall claddings of timber (see below).
Wall elements of prefabricated houses frequently consist of a timber frame which is braced vertically or horizontally

according to its size. It is then panelled in with thermal retaining materials. Timber boarding is often used as an external cladding which where possible is taken over the joints without a break. On the internal face, the panels can likewise be clad with timber strips or panels which then form the actual walls of the room. With reference to damp diffusion it appears to be expedient to avoid vacuums in the centre of such walls. Frequently timber panels for assembly houses are one storey high and about 1·40 m wide; windows and doors can be inserted in the works and delivered with the wall component. Other external wall elements which are one storey high and up to 7 m wide are only relatively thin thanks to their good thermal retention, and consequently are light and easy to transport. It is even possible for complete rooms or houses to be produced in the factory.

External wall claddings of timber

Apart from the traditional native softwoods (pine, fir and larch), increasing use is being made of hardwoods like oak and various tropical woods. The many species of wood used today require exact knowledge of their technical and visual properties and their suitability, especially regarding weather-resistance, dimensional stability and their surface properties. The individual timbers are often known by a variety of names: sometimes they are simply named according to other timbers of a similar appearance with which they have no more in common than their colour. To some extent the properties of exotic woods are still unknown. This is especially true of the colouring, tannin, volatile oil, fats, waxes, resins, etc. These materials contribute to the aesthetic effect and to the chemical, physical and mechanical properties of the timber. Since the effectiveness of such timbers has not yet had adequate research, it is imperative to keep to the instructions for treatment of the surface, as stated by the merchant.

In any case only those species of wood should be used on the exterior of buildings which have shown themselves to be suitable in past experience and about whose properties sufficient knowledge is available. As well as an attractive colour and graining, they must have high natural weather-resistance and good endurance, and must contain no substance which would have a detrimental effect apart from those substances which can be isolated. One must also guard against attack by fungi and bear in mind the extent of shrinking and the difficulty of working the timber.

The exotic woods in the following table are suitable for use on external walls by reason of their properties – partly according to pre-treatment. (However, there are other possible suitable timbers.)

Timbers for use externally must not only be correctly chosen but must also be suitably formed and properly combined one with another or with other building materials. Timber on external surfaces is exposed to frequent changes of weather whose influences can cause shrinkage, swelling or warping. The most appropriate application is a split surface such as we know in timber shingles of larch or cedar in which the slices (cut across the rings) are protected by lapping and the whole tile is ventilated.

Timber must always be used in boarding in such a way that it can be thoroughly ventilated. External walls of timber must

Name	Country of origin	Colour
Agba (Tola)	Tropical West Africa (Congo, Nigeria)	Yellow-brownish
Alerce (Chilean Yew)	South America (Chile)	Reddish-purple patches
Belinga	Tropical West and Central Africa	Golden yellow
Carolina Pine	South-east North America	Yellowish
Oregon Pine	Western North America Canada to Mexico	Yellowish-brown
Doussié (Afzelia)	Tropical Africa (Ghana to Uganda)	Yellowish-brown
Iroko (Kambala)	Tropical West and East Africa (Sierra Leone, Uganda)	Yellowish-brown
Kokrodua (Afrormosia)	Tropical West Africa (Ivory Coast to Congo)	Greenish-yellow to brown
Landa	Tropical West Africa (Sierra Leone to Congo)	Reddish-brown
Longleaf pine (Red pine, pitch pine)	South-east North America	Yellowish-reddish brown
Niangon	Tropical West Africa (coast of Guinea from Sierra Leone to Gabon)	Brown
Niové	Tropical West Africa (coast of Guinea from southern Nigeria to Angola)	Orange brown
Sequoia (Redwood)	West coast of North America (Southern Oregon to central California)	Light red
Sipo	Tropical West and East Africa (Liberia to Uganda)	Reddish-brown
Tchitola	Tropical West Africa (coast of Guinea)	Brown
Teak	South-east Asia (India to Indo-china, Java)	Brown
Thuja (Western Red Cedar)	Western North America (Alaska to California)	Reddish-brown
Yang	South-east Asia (Philippines and Indonesia)	Reddish-brown often with a purple bloom

also be back ventilated at least in one direction, but preferably in two, especially if the external face is to be painted or varnished and thus made air tight. The layers of strawboard frequently found directly behind the timber cladding are unsuitable in this position: they belong behind the air gaps.

Rainwater must be able to flow away quickly and without any obstruction. Also adequate clearance from the ground to avoid splashing is necessary. Vertical boarding disperses the water better than horizontal boarding on which the water's adhesion has greater effect. If the boarding is horizontal and tongued and grooved at least the front edges must be chamfered. Firs should be left rough-sawn on their surface if they are not to be painted with an agent forming a film. In each case the edges of planed deciduous woods are prone to fracture (splintering at the edges).

Timber cut across the rings requires special attention because the heart will be exposed at certain times and will become 20 times more damp than the outer rings. Such a conversion of timber is therefore to be avoided. Cross-cut timber must be covered from the top and underneath it must be splayed off upwards to the interior (forming a drip). Between the cross-cut timber and the covering there should always be a distance of 1 to 2 cm for ventilation. It must always be possible to have easy access to all cross-cut timber areas for after-treatment; likewise, the cross-cut drips should always be accessible. The individual strips of the cladding should be kept as narrow as possible in order to limit the working of the timber (according to the species, up to 100 mm wide and not less than 17 mm thick).

For fixings, which wherever possible should be covered, stainless screws or nails are recommended. Boards over 80 mm wide should be doubly fixed at each point. Wall claddings of timber lend themselves to prefabrication in a workshop because the moisture in the timber can be worked and jointed quicker and better with mechanical aids. It is also more expedient to apply the first protective coat in a works (possibly by a dip process).

Surface treatment of timber used externally

Timber used on external walls should be protected by means of surface treatment against weathering effects, damage from plants or animals, and possibly also against fire. The chosen wood, its construction and its surface treatment should so harmonize that a coat of paint or an impregnation not only protects the wood but also improves its visual appearance. Untreated wood exposed to weathering changes its colour under the influence of light and damp: usually it becomes grey within one year. Many deciduous woods bleach, others blacken.

The use of oil, as in those woods which are naturally oily (for example, Sipo and Teak) has not proved successful for external use. Timber which is merely oiled is not adequately protected against weather and also shows dirt easily. Under no circumstances should one feign a weathering patina on new timber by using water soluble uni-lacquer paints. If the timber is to be given a weathered appearance from the beginning, this can only be achieved by oily timber protective agents.

Impregnating coats: most timbers are liable to be attacked both by insects and fungi. The sapwood of all pine and some firs is especially prone to "blueing" (a bluish discolouring of the timber caused by a fungus). Such timbers must be primed first of all with an appropriate timber protective agent.

Water-repellent agents on a water or oil binding agent base (tar, bitumen or chlor-naphthalene base) can be included amongst impregnating coats. The desire for untreated matt timber cladding can be satisfied by means of pigmented impregnating agents (also called "azure" colours). They are varnished on in colours similar to timber. But such colours do not obliterate the timber graining.

Impregnating coats are well suited to rough-sawn claddings of fir. As far as it is technically possible, the dip process should always be used. In this process firs are impregnated twice, deciduous woods three times. Lacquers should be evenly distributed over the timber surface. If, after application, one wipes the surface with a cloth, the hard annular rings stand out better against the light ones. The disadvantage of such surface treatment is that in time the impregnating agent is partly washed away by downpours of rain and that the timber must therefore be treated again, according to type and coating material, in one to three years, if one wishes to avoid premature greying. Naturally then one simple coat is sufficient. Nevertheless one cannot preserve the natural wood colouring, especially of light-coloured woods (pine, Scotch fir and pitch pine). The lighter the pigment the quicker they become grey. Therefore colourless impregnations are mostly unsuitable for external walls. Finally, dust catches more easily on the raw surface.

Transparent lacquers: these include pore-closing and film-forming surfaces in which natural timber colours and grainings are preserved. Usually lacquering accentuates the graining and colouring. Even when the surface has been treated, every type of timber changes in time under the influence of ultra-violet sun rays as well as under the effect of acids in the air. This is especially true of exotic timbers. Most kinds of wood deepen in colour; some go yellow and coloured timbers can change their tone. Thus for example the yellowish-brown Afzelia darkens to a strong reddish colour and the yellowish Iroko darkens to an intense brown colour. Dark woods can become slightly lighter in tone.

Transparent lacquers give a glossy surface on which dust does not accumulate. They do indeed cost more in labour than impregnations but on the other hand they do not usually need retreating for four or five years. But damage to the edges and other fractures must however rapidly be dealt with. Sal ammoniac is suitable for cleaning or roughening up. Transparent lacquers should only be applied to planed wood, where possible to heartwood in which the edges are slightly broken (no knotty or resinous timbers!). The timber should not have more than 15 per cent moisture content when being treated with pore-closing and film-forming surfaces. Tropical deciduous woods should contain even less (under 12 per cent). The cladding strips should be primed on all sides before being put together; this is essential for the permanency of the protective coat.

Timber species which contain substances which can be leached out should be isolated before priming, because these substances become liquid under the influence of heat and deposit themselves on the surface. They can discolour on application (by the so-called bleeding, that is the diffusion of soluble colouring materials of the wood which penetrate the coating under simultaneous change of colour) or they can check the drying of the application and prevent, or even lead to the destruction of, a lacquer film. D. D. lacquers, or washing out and brushing out by nitro-combinations according to the manufacturer's instructions, have proved themselves as isolating agents. After the first coat all sides of the timber (including the back face and especially the cross-cut timber sides) should be pre-lacquered. A satisfactory weather-fast coat can only be achieved if the total build-up consists of four individually applied layers of coating, each of which must properly dry out. The application instructions of the lacquer manufacturer should always be adhered to. Only products of the same manufacturer should be used for the various layers.

Covering coats: they are not usual on external timber of new buildings but they are possible, and can give a very suitable visual effect. Here also the surfaces will first of all be impregnated with an oily timber protective agent and finally coated with three covering coats (including the lacquering).

K External walls of glass

In modern architecture glass is not only used for windows, it is also frequently used to form the external walls in order to give these the airiness, lightness and transparency of windows.

But glass is also a building, mechanical and weather-resistant material: it is resistant to acids, alkalies, salts and fats. Its smooth surface does not catch dust or dirt. It is anticorrosive and if it has been colour-impregnated with minerals it is also colour-fast. Apart from cleaning there are no maintenance costs whatsoever. As a smooth non-porous material it is perfect protection against damp from the exterior but at the same time it prevents vapour transference from interior to exterior.

Plain glass: glass tiles and glass wall slabs

With plain glass, damp diffusion must be catered for by means of special measures. Whether glass wall slabs stand free in front of the external masonry or whether an insulating slab is inserted, or yet again whether they are applied to the wall by means of glues and mastics is dependent on two factors: the nature of the glass panels and the purpose of the building. One uses larger glass wall slabs in a double-skinned back ventilated construction.

Opaque (that is, mass-produced coloured non-transparent) glass is used with a polished or post-treated surface and ribbed reverse side. The glass is melted at high temperatures and processed into large panes from 15 to 16 mm thick from which glass wall panels of 2·50 x 5·0 m, glass tiles of 15 x 15, 15 x 20, 15 x 30 and 20 x 30 cm and medium-size mosaic of 5 x 5 cm, are cut. Compound glass panels with a coloured intermediary layer of foil and colourless and transparent glass (for example, armoured glass, and armoured ornamental glass) are also available; when using the latter, the wall behind them must be painted or otherwise applied with the desired colours. Dark-coloured glass stores infra-red sun rays considerably and in the process heats itself to breaking point. Thus for all darker colours in glass, intermediary layer or applications, and the reflection of these back colourings, have all to be considered carefully to avoid breakage. In principle, therefore, dark-coloured glass should not be used in large panels on façades receiving a lot of sunshine, without having special safety properties, not even in small slabs without additional precautions. In order to avoid this difficulty it is better to use pre-stretched glass.

With industrial production of coloured enamelled pre-stretched glass, a standard safety glass was brought on to the market, which made possible numerous constant colour tones. Colours of silicate enamel have the same properties as glass, i.e. they are light-fast and constant. From the technical point of view this type of glass offers a high impact-resistance, shock-resistance and compositional strength, conditioned by its high bending strength of 2000 kg/cm². If this glass does break, on account of a powerful pressure, the glass forms into equal small fragments and not into dangerous slivers. The glass is unaffected by temperature variations up to 300° C. Glass tiles are put directly onto the external wall in tufa-lime mortar or in a special mastic. Glass tile claddings have

relatively few joints and thus form an external skin which is well-nigh impervious, and which hinders damp diffusion from the interior to the exterior. This vapour barrier lies on the cold side of the external wall and is thus wrongly placed from the technical point of view. The external wall must therefore be built up in such a way that the air's water vapour cannot pour down the inside face of the wall as condensation. This requires an internal vapour barrier. In living rooms with their high humidity (breathing, cooking, bathing) this returns and leads to an unbearable rise in humidity. Furthermore it must be borne in mind that after completion walls still undergo changes (shrinking, creeping and setting): the glass tiles break or fall off. It would certainly be possible to improve their adhesion with a mastic setter but this, on the other hand, would consolidate the external skin yet more.

Glass tiles should not be fixed until tensions in the masonry have died away. They must be laid deeply so that no air pockets result where damp from exterior or interior could collect. In general, glass tiles are not used for external walls of rooms constantly inhabited but rather for shops, display windows, etc.

Larger glass tiles – so-called glass wall panels – can be placed in front of the external wall as back ventilated cladding (weather protection). The face of the wall and the reverse of the panels should be at least 30 mm apart. The air between cladding and wall is linked with the external air so that adequate air circulation is guaranteed between the panels. (Air vents of at least 60 x 50 mm at distances of 100 mm on the lower frame casing and 50 mm on the upper horizontal one.) Glass wall panels can either be set in metal frames or timber frames or into normal window frames with mastic. Under certain circumstances the side frames are dispensed with and the glass wall frames are put into metal rebates in neoprene sections.

As the glass wall panels are only held on the edges, they must be able to take up wind loading and other static and mechanical loadings and, especially in tall blocks, be able to resist suction. The same criterion is valid for the choice of dark glass as for glass tiles. Partial shade caused by projecting parts of the building or its framework can also lead to temperature differences within the glass panel. These difficulties can be avoided if one uses pre-stretched glass whose ability to resist temperature variations and mechanical stresses is four to five times higher than for normal flat glass.

Glass mosaic

Glass mosaic is available as an industrial mosaic (2 x 2 cm) or medium-size mosaic (5 x 5 cm) pieces. There are a proportionally high number of joints, in industrial mosaic about 10 to 15 per cent. It is thus suitable for external walls of inhabited rooms if no very high humidity is expected in them.

Prefabricated mosaic is mostly available, ready to use, in panels 31 cm². The pieces are either stuck face down on to sheets of paper which can be torn off after the pieces have been set, or they are linked on the reverse side with an elastic adhesive layer which remains in the mortar.

To set industrial mosaic following recommended processes: the undersurface should be plumb and well-aligned (if necessary a foundation render 1:3 should be applied). Then a bedding render consisting of 9 parts fine-grained river sand, 3 parts normal cement and 1 part completely slaked lime, should be applied approximately 8 mm thick. The mosaic panels, which are uniformly coated with thinned jointing mortar, should be lightly tapped into the render whilst still soft. The paper can be removed by wetting it and then any necessary corrections can be made before the surface is cleaned with water. After one or two days the mosaic is washed down with a solution containing 10 per cent hydrochloric acid and then thoroughly rinsed off with water. Glass mosaic, having almost unlimited possibilities of colour, fulfils all requirements regarding safety and insulation. It is not difficult to work with and requires almost no precautions concerning possible expansion or tensile considerations.

Glass building elements, glass bricks

Glass building elements as external walls, used for panelling skeleton constructions, are multi-layered. A pane of pre-stretched coloured safety glass forms the outer face and, if it breaks, will disintegrate into small fragments. A layer of thermal insulation provides the necessary thermal protection and an inner barrier layer, which must also enclose the edges, prevents this thermal layer from being dampened by vapour diffusion from the interior.

This inner barrier can be dispensed with if foamed glass is used, because such glass is also in effect a vapour barrier. Thus, for example, Opal building elements are combined into one panel consisting of a coloured enamelled one-pane safety glass sheet, with a thermal retention layer of foamed glass and an internal gypsum board with a special adhesive. The range of colours of Color-glass (mirror glass with a polished or beaded surface or machine-stamped) is extensive. The colours of the sheets vary but little, only influenced by the thickness of the glass, its pattern or the annealing process. The thickness of the external layer of glass is dependent on its desired size (a thickness of at least 5 to 12 mm). The maximum size of slabs at the moment is 1,670 x 3,200 mm. The standard element is usually about 52 mm thick and weighs approximately 30 kg/m² (thermal transfer figure K: about 0·96 kcal/m²h° C). The thermal layer on framed glass is 38 mm thick. The internal face is a 6·5 mm thick plasterboard slab whose exposed face is tempered by a coat of paint.

For assembly: glass building elements can be inserted into timber, metal, masonry or concrete, but may not be stretched into the rebate, rather deeply penetrating the mastic. The distance between the edge of the element and the rebate should be at least 5 mm. The intermediate space between the surface of the element and the rear face of the rebate or the beading should be at least 3 mm. The rebate should be 18 mm across. Its depth can be deduced from the thickness of the element and the mastic bed of 2 to 3 mm.

Where there are special stresses (high blocks or strong winds) an external impervious type of element should be used which retains high value elastic qualities. The elements must rest at the bottom on 5 mm thick bearing blocks of oily hardwood or other suitable material which, when the base length is 60 to 80 mm long, must correspond in width to the thickness of the element. On the side, and in the plane of the elements, small spacers should be inserted.

Non-hardening tough plastic mastics, which retain this characteristic between +80° C and –20° C and adhere perfectly to both element and rebate, are suitable. The rebates and elements must be clean before glazing and be dry and free of dust. For timber window frames the rebates have to be primed with suitable paints so that no oil can pass from mastic to wood. The same stands if glass panels are placed in front of masonry.

If several elements are fixed hard up one to another, then an internal surrounding gasket of a T-profile is recommended. For external sealing, proofing substances on a Thiokol base, can be suggested, whilst internal sealing can be achieved with a spray coat of proofing on a butyl base, amongst others. For fire-limiting elements, the above-mentioned surrounding gaskets have a tongued and grooved form.

Glass bricks serve for flat or curved external walls which do not require high thermal insulation. They are produced by a pressing process, white or multi-coloured glass bodies, which consist of one piece (full glass bricks) or of several interconnected pieces (hollow glass bricks). The internal or external exposed faces are smooth or variously textured by stamping. By this means a decorative light-distributing effect is achieved. They must only be loaded with their self-weight parallel to their surface.

L External wall surfaces of or including metal

Steel sheets have been used, as is well known, for a long times, especially in industrial and warehouse buildings, for external wall construction or cladding. In individual cases they are sometimes used for other building types.

Unprotected steel rusts under the influence of air and damp so that its surface must be protected against corrosion and the effects of destructive electrolytic action prevented.

The reason for steel rusting is the tendency of all ignoble metals, as for example iron, zinc or aluminium, to return to their original form. These (energy-rich) metals are liberated from naturally occurring ores (low energy) by metallurgical processes. By means of corrosion they return from their energy-rich state to their original low energy state. In general, there are two possibilities for protection against corrosion: 1. One can protect the surface of the steel by means of metal and non-metal, organic and inorganic, coatings (passive corrosion protection). These are galvanised coats (zinc covering with a coat of paint), films of synthetic materials, or enamels. However, all such protective layers must be constantly watched over and also renewed from time to time.

2. In order to save the considerable cost involved by these processes, techniques were developed which aim at making the steel itself stainless: by alloying with other metals, and thus preventing corrosion right from the outset (active protection against corrosion).

Furthermore, steel constructions must be thoroughly executed so that at no point can water be captive over a long period or penetrate into parts which cannot be protected against the formation of rust. Especial care must be taken to prevent possible formations of rust also at those points which are particularly exposed to the effects of damp as, for example, all parts near the ground.

A film coating on steel surfaces

Paints on steel sheet: the simplest, most economical and therefore the method most frequently used today for protecting steel sheets from corrosion is to paint the surface. In architecture the coat of paint fulfils a double purpose: it protects against atmospheric and chemical influences, and simultaneously serves to ennoble the surface.

Paints on an oil base, in normal atmospheric conditions (i. e. no effect from acid vapours, excessive humidity, etc.) are still considered to be the best protection. The formation of the stable coat influences the pigment suspended in the oil by means of mechanical consolidation, but above all by means of physical and chemical reactions in the drying process. As far as a transposition is possible, above all basic pigments with oil or of the free fatty acids contained in any oil, "metal soaps" form themselves when the coating agent settles, which hasten the drying and increase water-resistance. This is the case when white lead, lead chromate, and zinc oxide are used, but particularly when red lead is used. Top coats containing linseed oil have a favourable effect on the weather-resistance and on resistance to slight chemical influences. The basic principle to be observed is that steel areas must be free of rust, fat and dirt; painting over rust only leads to further formations of rust under the paint.

The coating consists usually of two undercoats containing pigments which protect against rust, and two top coats. Each layer must be thoroughly dry and hard before the next is applied. This building up in four layers should be used everywhere where the coating is exposed to any special effects from chemicals, steam, sea water and other corrosives.

The total thickness of the layer must be at least 125 My. Usually, however, the thickness of a layer requires at least 160 My. (A single coating with an agent containing oil and fine grained pigments on a non-absorbent surface produces a thickness of layer of 20 to 60 My, a single spray application producing a thickness of 5 to 15 My. So that the usual four coats today applied by brush for protection against rust, form a layer of 140 to 180 My.)

For very exposed surfaces the type of coating agent must be correspondingly suitable and if necessary, several top coats must be applied; in fact, the thinner the build-up of application the less possible is it for gases and water vapours to penetrate and attack the metal. However, it should be borne in mind that several thin coats dried, and applied one after the other, are more permanent than one thick one: with the increasing thickness of the individual layer the resistance and adhesion reduce. Especial attention should be given to ensuring that the application on the edges is just as thick as on the surface. The paint specialist knows how this can be achieved in practice.

Zinced sheets with coatings

Instead of protective coats it is far better on the site to zinc the sheets and profiles, primarily because coats of paint easily become porous and cracked in time on account of mechanical stresses and temperature variations. The rust which results at such points can cause the paint to peel off.

Zincing under high temperatures, as alloying of the basic metal, provides an essentially better protection against corrosion than several priming coats, and costs almost the same, including prior sandblasting.

Steel sheets for external wall claddings are either galvanised or zinced under high temperatures. The zinc forms a natural oxide layer (basic zinc carbonate) which protects against further corrosion. However, in time this layer becomes grey and unattractive. For this reason it is recommended that in every case a coat of paint should be applied even if no particular colour effects are originally intended. After all, the coat of paint protects the layer of zinc itself.

A prerequisite for the permanency of the coating is good adhesion to the zinc base. Not every coating adheres straightaway to freshly electrolyted or zinced-under-heat surfaces. The surfaces to be painted must be previously treated (degreased, mechanical rubbing-up, coating with an adhesive layer) or special coating must be used (see table below) which harmonizes with the base. For the priming, the pigments should not contain graphite or lead (with the exception of calcium plumbate). Thus, coatings on freshly zinced steel, in contrast to coatings on unzinced steel, may not be carried out with red lead. However, such difficulties do not occur with all zinc surfaces in which the zinc oxidation layer acts as isolation, nor do they always affect the coats following the primer.

Generally, if linseed oil paints or alkyd resin lacquer paints are used, one primer and one top coat are sufficient. If a so-called "wash" primer is used to improve the adhesion of the coating, then two top coats are neccessary. This is also necessary for all applications of white or brightly coloured tones.

Damaged parts in the zinced-by-heat metal, which could occur as a result of damage in transit, in assembly, or in welding as well as through corrosion from long exposure to weather, can be improved if the surface is thoroughly cleaned or derusted and then fully coated with a zinc dust coating material (also wrongly termed "cold zincing"). After this process, paint can be applied.

Enamelled steel sheets

Enamel is a mass resulting from smelting or cohesion (smelting not fully carried out). Mainly it is a glassy solidified material of inorganic (in the main oxide) composition, which is smelted on to the metal in one or several layers.

Enamel has good mechanical strength and is therefore resistant to thrust and impact; also, a number of forms are possible.

Enamelled steel sheet panels are colour-fast and resistant to corrosion. They are either fastened in front of the external wall and back ventilated, or they are processed into compound elements with a coloured external coating. In such cases any desired colour, with either a matt or shiny finish, is possible.

As a result of its smooth surface, an enamelled sheet hardly shows the dirt; it therefore always retains a clean and pleasant appearance and at the same time requires little care and attention.

No.	Surface to be coated	Pre-treatment	Corrosive adhesive ground	Primer for		Finishing coats
				Domestic building	Industrial building	
1	Zincing by heat Galvanising	a) Weathered surfaces not previously painted to be roughed up by abrasives b) Roughing-up of new surfaces by means of a 10 per cent hydrochloric acid water mix and then rinsed with water c) De-greasing, with the following mix: Tetrachlorcarbon 5 vols Hydrochloric acid 5 vols Toluol 30 vols Spirits 60 vols 100 vols Apply with a brush, wipe off with a cloth and rinse with water	Two tank wash-primer adhesive ground	Zinc chromate, zinc white, colour zinc oxide in linseed oil varnish, fatty oil lacquers, oil-alkyd resin lacquers, etc.	Zinc chromate, zinc oxide, zinc dust or zinc powder in styrol alkyd lacquers, chlor- and cyclo-rubber lacquers, epoxy resin lacquers, vinyl resin lacquers, etc. (Old partly rusted sheets should be primed with linseed oil or alkyd resin red lead after thorough de-rusting)	Binding agents for domestic building or industrial building with all weather-resistant, lightfast, white and coloured pigments, coating, emulsions and dispersions are likewise suitable as binding agents
2	Zinc spray layers	No special pretreatment necessary. Any dirt marks merely washed or rubbed off	Like 1	Like 1, however, lead-free coating agents		Like 1

Steel sheets covered in layers of synthetic materials

Such steel sheets can, like enamelled steel sheets, be put in front of the external wall as weather protection or be used as wall elements with a coloured "external skin". In the case of steel sheets covered with p.v.c. the synthetic material is so firmly combined with the steel that deformations can occur without the p.v.c. loosening or being destroyed. The synthetic material layer forms a weather-resistant protection against corrosion. For this purpose, zinced cold strip steel is used, 1·25 to 1·5 mm thick. The sheets are delivered flat or in standard profiles. The synthetic material layers, coated on one or both sides with p.v.c., are available in numerous colours and with varied surface texturing.

External wall panels and claddings of non-rusting steel

Non-rusting steel – also known as "rust-free" steel, "rust-free" noble steel, or "noble steel rust-free" – is on the market with various trade names. Thus one distinguishes between chrome steels and chrome nickel steels. These steels offer all the constructional possibilities of non-alloyed steel with the further advantage that they are resistant to corrosion; by reason of their chemical composition, they behave like noble metals. For external wall cladding, their surface does not need to be specially protected, so that the metallic gleam of the steel can be fully appreciated. The visual appearance can be further intensified by texturing the steel sheet, resulting in light and shade effects. Also to be considered for external wall claddings are chrome nickel steels. A few comments on the individual types:

a) "Stainless steel 18 to 8", Stock no. 4300: basic type of all the chrome nickel steels which are called "18 to 8" steels. This steel is easily formed and resistant to external atmosphere. It is therefore suitable for external claddings. It is not to be recommended for welded constructions because after welding it is necessary to anneal it, which usually cannot be carried out on prefabricated parts.

b) "Stainless steel 18 to 9", Stock no. 4301: 18 to 8 chrome nickel steel with the same corrosion and working properties as Stock no. 4300. However, it is also suitable for welding since it is not necessary to anneal it afterwards.

c) "Stainless steel 18 to 10 to 2", Stock no. 4401: developed from the 18 to 8 group, chrome nickel molybdenum steel ("18 to 10 to 2") has a specially high corrosion resistance. It also resists the attack of atmospheric chloride and sulphuric acid and is therefore suitable for buildings near a coast as well as in the vicinity of chemical and heavy industries. Its forming properties are the same as those for Stock no. 4301. This steel can also be welded without post-annealing. Both "18 to 8" steels and "18 to 10 to 2" steel are non-magnetic. However, if they are very much re-formed, light magnetism occurs. They are recognisable by their yellowish-silver gleam. Stainless steel can be used in very thin sheets on account of its high strength. Cold-rolled sheet and strip or profiles and tubes formed from these are the materials suitable for building. German manufacturers deliver strips in widths of up to 970 mm (called 1,000 mm) and individual steel sheets with a maximum size of 1,500 x 3,000 mm. The sheet thicknesses usable on the site are generally between 0·8 and 1·5 mm. As well as flat sheets, round, flat, square and profiled steels are produced in warm-rolled, pressed, extruded or polished finishes as well as shaped, beaten or cast pieces.

The choice of surface finish does not only depend on the architectural effect. It also essentially determines the maintenance costs and the permanency of the cladding. External wall claddings are not only exposed to air and acid but also to dust. The air, especially of large cities, contains innumerable metal particles which settle on stainless steel, begin to rust there, and thus give the impression that the wall cladding itself is rusting.

It is therefore not only important occasionally to clean the surface later on (see below) but it should be tested from the outset which surface finish will give the best visual effect in each case and at the same time is expedient with respect to the low maintenance.

Dust and dirt adhere less to smooth surfaces; such surfaces also encourage self-cleaning in rain. Highly-polished steel surfaces can however cause powerful reflections, when the slightest unevenness can be seen on them.

Cold-rolled sheets and strips with especially suitable architectural surfaces:

1) Process IIIb: cold-rolled, heat-treated, pickled. The pickled surface gives a matt effect (similar to etched glass) and hardly gives any reflection. Although it has a pleasing appearance there are certain objections to its use: if the sheets are deformed, traces of working have to be reckoned with, which can detract from its uniform appearance. Furthermore this pickled surface is, even with stainless steel, most susceptible to finger marks. It is certainly possible to remove these, but in the long run it is an expensive process. Where a surface is required to give a uniform appearance, as for example at close quarters, such a surface is not suitable.

2) Process IIIc: cold-rolled, heat-treated, pickled and pressed. In this process sheets and strips are flattened (roller-polished) directly following the pickling, between high gloss polished rollers; the resulting cold strengthening is inconsiderable. The very smooth surface shows hardly any dirt in the open air. IIIc sheets are frequently used, for example in the USA, for spandrel claddings, windowless walls, or roof finishes.

3) Process IV: polished. This description is a collective term for polished noble steel sheets. Their surfaces reflect, possess considerable visual uniformity and are suitable everywhere where the appearance is very important (such as shop windows, doors). The fineness of the polish is dependent on the graining of the polishing paper which normally extends from coarse grain 80 to fine grain 400. The usual grain steps for a noble steel are: grain 80, 150, 240, 320, 400. In building a fine polish with a 320 grain is to be recommended. To some extent the fineness of the polished surface also depends on the skill of the operator. In the specification, therefore, it is expedient to proceed from work patterns.

4) Process V: polished. In this group various finenesses of polish can be produced by means of various polishing methods. Frequently matt polished or brushed surfaces are used for architecture. In the latter process brushes of stainless steel wire or ones with natural or synthetic bristles are used. All these surfaces have a matt, silky sheen according to the hardness of the bristle used and the fineness of grain of the polishing paste. Glossy polishes are usually produced with a buffing disc, a disc which revolves and which is covered with pieces of fabric lapped over, similar to a book wrapper. Lately, electro-polishing is gaining importance in the building trade. In mechanical polishing the surface unevennesses are polished away or flattened, whilst with electro-polishing only the external layer is removed: the bumps are more easily removed than the hollows. This process produces a shiny surface. However, it does require great experience and up to now can only be carried out by a few technicians. It is well suited to the treatment of many small parts and here distinguishes itself by comparatively low costs.

Polished brushed or matt polished surfaces can be especially recommended to the architect since they show the character of the noble material to full advantage. Which of these finishes one uses depends primarily on the method of the surface treatment.

Flat wall elements are only occasionally used for wall cladding. They are easily deformed during working and assembly; they are also exposed to considerable stresses as a result of temperature variations. Flat panels, if they are not sufficiently stiffened by combining them with another material, must be of a minimum thickness. The following table shows maximum dimensions for building parts of flat "18 to 8" sheets without a supporting structure:

Thickness (in mm)	0,4	0,6	0,8	1,0	1,2	1,4	1,6	1,8	2,0
The maximum length of matt surfaces (mm)		80	120	160	200	240	280	320	360	400
Maximum length of polished surfaces (mm)	60	90	120	150	180	210	240	270	300

For profile wall elements the same sheets can be used. The additional labour costs can be balanced out by economies in the material.

For the polishing of flat sheets the following processes could be used: rounding off the edges; pressing and deep extrusion; forming a channel on the edge; turning and stamping it. In the first process the surfaces are treated before they are worked and then protected with stretched skin which is not removed until after assembly. The second process is especially suitable for the production of a larger number of equal slab elements with a strongly profiled surface. For production reasons the elements must not have any sharp edges, so that rounded edges of the profiles are characteristic of these. Finally, rollers can also imprint certain patterns or profiles. If such slabs are used as external wall cladding, then one should only choose a pattern whose hollows will not be collecting points for dirt or damp.

Smooth wall elements require less care and cleaning than decorative patterned ones. But in principle the façade should be carefully watched and cleaned even if stainless steel is used. With the exception of copper, all other metals and alloys do indeed lose their good appearance and their metallic character because corrosion-resistance depends primarily on the formation of an oxide layer to protect the surface. However, if foreign bodies settle on the surface, it can be damaged by means of electro-chemical reactions. Therefore dust and particles of dirt must be removed with wire brushes from stainless steel. To clean the surface one can use a cleansing agent based on a phosphorus acid or an appropriate alkaline. When all metal claddings are being designed into a building, installations should be provided by means of which the façades can safely be cleaned.

Light metal on external walls

The advantages of aluminium are its lightness and its ease of handling.

By means of appropriate additives, alloys can be produced with varying hardness, breaking and tensile strength and varying weather-resistance to industrial or sea-coast atmosphere. Within a short period a firmly adhering, thin, non-water-soluble oxide skin forms as a result of atmospheric conditions; this skin protects the metal from further corrosion. However, this causes the shiny metal surface to become grey, dull and unattractive. Thus, aluminium with an untreated surface can be used anywhere where no special visual effects is desired, e. g. in wall claddings for agricultural and industrial buildings.

If, on the other hand, façades, windows, entrance doors, wall claddings and fittings are to be of decorative aluminium, then there is a whole series of proven processes which will permanently preserve the natural metal sheen, or will achieve coloured effects. Even if the atmosphere is especially aggressive, for example near coke kilns, the aluminium surface can be resistant. To achieve this there are the following possibilities: anodic oxidation; chemical oxidation; paint or stoved lacquering; and enamelling.

Aluminium sheets can be remodelled into profiled strips or wall panels which can be formed into pyramid shapes by pressing. Also one can turn it into many decorative surface patterns. Nowadays, aluminium sheets can also be cast, which presents wide possibilities for architectural design, e.g. a projecting relief with a naturally cast skin and with it a coloured enamel base and so on. In connexion with insulation, wall elements can also be manufactured of aluminium.

Paints, stoved lacquers, enamels and coatings of synthetic materials

The first step is to clean the metal of foreign bodies before it is coated. This also holds good for the renewal of old paints. Any patches of dirt, grease or oil reduce the paint's adhesion. Anodised aluminium parts should not be coated. Untreated aluminium, after thorough cleansing, and after having been roughened with fine sandpaper and with the usual trade cleansing agents, should be coated with an adhesive undercoat (wash primer); this is followed by a further primer, and one or two top coats in the desired colour. Lead paints (e.g. red lead and white lead) are unsuitable, although they are used for painting steel.

By combining aluminium with other metals, e.g. at junctions with steel and similar materials, one has to be prepared for corrosion (if the metals are not separated) as a result of electrolytic action as soon as damp (especially sea water) penetrates. The same is true of items such as screws, rivets and bolts of other metals. A thorough coat of "wash" primer and zinc chromate, after assembly, on all parts no longer visible, will provide good protection. After the parts have been joined together, several carefully applied top coats give the best protection against the penetration of damp to these joints and thus prevent corrosion. Aluminium must likewise be isolated from concrete and fresh render (very alkaline) chiefly because it is very sensitive to alkali. Before the aluminium is fixed, it is recommended (e.g. on the reverse sides of signs) that a coat of neutral phenol-free bitumen be applied. Stove lacquering with polymerising synthetic resins is characterised by its especially good weather-resistance. The manufacturers guarantee it for 15 to 20 years. If new coats are applied its duration can be increased still further. Stove lacquering is much less expensive than anodisation or enamelling, because the stove-lacquered aluminium sheets can be profiled afterwards (by means of rollers) and then cut into

the desired lengths. Like steel sheets, it is possible to coat aluminium sheets with p.v.c.

By enamelling aluminium wall panels (as steel sheets) various coloured effects can be obtained. The enamel is weather-resistant and colour-fast. It can be drilled and cut.

Anodised wall panels

The oxide layer produced by this process strengthens the natural surface of the aluminium and preserves its sheen. Such a layer is indissolubly combined with the aluminium.

The aluminium layer can be colourless, then the metallic sheen can be preserved. But it can also be intrinsically coloured. Apart from black and metal colours like brass, gold, bronze and copper, there is also a range of yellow, red, blue and green tones available. The individual colours are obtained by means of various aluminium alloys and by means of various inorganic and organic pigments. The oxide layer is in each case more or less light-fast. But it does have a high weather-resistance and abrasion strength.

The weather-resistance of aluminium coverings can also be strengthened by coatings (spraying or dipping) with suitable colourless synthetic resin lacquers without its characteristic appearance suffering. These lacquers can prevent electrolytic reactions of metallic powder on the surface of the oxide layer and also preclude chemical attacks from mortar and concrete should the aluminium cladding come into contact with such alkaline-reactive materials. This should be given particular attention if aluminium parts must be fixed before the completion of masonry, concreting or rendering. To guard against aluminium parts being scratched or banged, it is best to build them in as late as possible. However, one must bear in mind the limited life of a lacquer and should not expect from it a long-term improvement of the protective effect of the oxide layer.

It should also be pointed out that even façades of anodic oxidised aluminium should be cleaned now and then. This is especially recommended in industrial areas where the atmosphere is especially dirty or aggressive. But under no circumstances should oxide-soluble render or cleansing agents (cleansing salts) be used for this purpose. Abrasive scratching agents or those having a mechanical effect should definitely be avoided.

General hints for using aluminium in façades

As a result of its wide range of application, aluminium very often comes into contact with other materials, so that some special measures are given here which would protect it under such circumstances.

If at all possible such mixed construction should be avoided and an aluminium construction should be executed without any additional help from other materials.

In a mixed construction, the arrangement of the aluminium or the other metal parts can considerably influence resistance to external effects. Narrow gaps, water pockets and other places where damp can gather should be avoided. Perspiration or rainwater must be able to run away unhindered. Those places which after completion are inaccessible should be especially carefully treated.

Where constructional parts are joined by screws, rivets or grooves, the space at the junction must above all be secured against corrosion resulting from penetrating damp. This is pertinent for the joining of the same metals and even more so for different metals. In this case the different electrolytic potential for attack is increased (so called galvanitic or contact corrosion). But non-metallic materials can also have a detrimental effect when combined with metallic materials if the points of contact are exposed to damp.

In buildings of metal construction, aluminium is frequently combined with steel, as for example when aluminium claddings, window and shop window constructions, are joined to the structural steel. These should be isolated by a coat of paint (under no circumstances red lead!), zincing or intermediate layers against the aluminium parts, because aluminium, when in contact with shiny or rusty steel, is attacked by alkaline reactions when damp penetrates. As protection against rust and corrosion the following coatings have proved successful: zinc, tin, cadmium, chromium and aluminium. The pamphlet entitled *Indications for the execution of aluminium façade* requires that constructional parts of steel should for this purpose be delivered with heat-zinc treatment or sandblasted and sprayed zinc surface and with a layer of at least 60 My.

Anodic oxidised aluminium parts must also be additionally protected when combined with other metals and if damp is to be expected.

Copper, bronze and brass, when combined with aluminium, lead especially to contact corrosion if there is a medium present which in any case would attack the above-named copper materials. If it should not be possible to avoid using these metals with aluminium, the aluminium must be carefully insulated. The combination of aluminium with copper in the open air should be avoided.

If aluminium is combined with non-metallic materials, it is certainly not possible for a contact element to form; on the other hand such materials can contain components which attack aluminium chemically. They can also be porous or hygroscopic and after damp has penetrated, can attack the contactor area of the aluminium parts. Therefore there are also corresponding measures to be taken for such mixed constructions.

It is important to isolate an aluminium part from the effect of damp cement, concrete and lime mortar by means of a coat of paint or intermediate layers.

Windows, shop windows and other parts of aluminium should be protected during rendering work from spillages of mortar and render by means of a removable lacquer film, because cement, concrete and lime mortar can easily corrode the aluminium during the setting process (alkaline-setting products). Once set and dry, they do not attack, although isolating is always expedient.

Bauxite cement and gypsum are in their dry condition neutral. But since they are porous and may become damp, isolating is necessary.

Even timber in its fresh state can attack; this is also true of some timber impregnating agents (e.g. sublimate, copper vitriol, zinc silicone fluoride). In addition it should be remembered that non-impregnated wood may also become damp. It is highly recommended that the wood is painted at the contact points; for this purpose, aluminium paint has proved successful. Chipboard should likewise be isolated.

Other metal wall elements

The steel and aluminium sheets for wall claddings, as described in the foregoing paragraphs, can be used in various constructions. On the one hand it is possible to use metal wall panels as cladding for walls or panelling of steel or reinforced concrete skeletons, in which case the wall panels only provide weather protection, whilst the thermal insulating and stability functions are performed by various other parts of the building. As a result of the increasing separation of functions in external walls – on the one hand bearing building materials, on the other hand thermal retaining and weather protecting – the metal wall panels have been further developed into spatially delineating wall elements. This is achieved by means of combining the metal wall plates with other materials which can provide thermal and sound insulation.

The numerous constructions possible for metal wall elements can be divided into the following main groups:
a) Spandrel panels
b) Infill panels of skeleton framed buildings, also in
c) Curtain walls
d) Self-bearing wall panels in curtain walls
e) Bearing wall panels in one-storey buildings

In each case the elements take on the functions of weather- and thermal-protection, to some extent also fire-protection, which would otherwise be taken care of by a masonry or concrete spandrel. If the spandrel takes on the function of thermal retention as well as the statical functions, then the sheet panel which are fixed externally and only form weather-protection (and which then must be back ventilated) in each case should be included in wall claddings and not in wall constructional elements.

The composition of wall elements is similar in all constructional systems, even though the architectonic and statical requirements can produce different finishes.

A sheet of steel or aluminium forms the external face of the wall element. These panels have the advantage of a jointless, dense external surface. They are light to transport and are also easily shaped.

Usually the same materials are used for the internal face as for the exterior, only with a different surface treatment. But in place of metal internal wall panels, one often finds internal claddings of asbestos cement panels, plasterboard, and other materials.

If however, materials with only low resistance to damp diffussion are used on the internal face of the wall element, it is necessary to put a damp barrier on the inner wall face. Between the two skins, there should be a thermal retention layer. It can consist of paper honeycomb sheets, inorganic materials like Perlite or vermiculite, mineral wool or glass wool slabs, or polystyrene hard foam slabs. Occasionally the intermediate space between the external and internal panels is also filled with Moltoprene. Recently, foamed glass has also been used for thermal retention, which combines good mechanical properties with the advantages of non-inflammability and absolute resistance to damp. As a consequence of its high resistance to vapour diffusion, no additional damp barrier is necessary on the internal face. It is important that the damp barrier, of all the other materials, is made damp and waterproof on all sides of the slab.

M General comments on painting external walls

In all the preceding chapters, the appropriate surface treatments and possible kinds of paint were discussed together with the actual materials. To summarize, there now follows a general section on colour tones, and a table showing the usability of paints.

Choice of colours (pigments suitable for façades)

The choice of colours for external wall paints should not be based purely on aesthetic reasons, but also on the knowledge of the limitations and possibilities of the material. If an architect does a watercolour or tempera sketch to suggest a colour scheme, then this cannot necessarily be realized in practice: frequently the demands placed upon façade paints with respect to light fastness, weather resistance etc. cannot be reproduced in the colours used in the design.

In detail the following points must be considered concerning the requisite properties of white and coloured pigments: a white or coloured pigment must be light-fast for a façade paint. By this one means that the tone does not change under the effect of natural or artificial light. Therefore, for external paints, only such pigments should be used which will neither grey, lighten or darken so that the colour effect aimed at in the design is guaranteed to last; this implies a limitation to certain tones provided by available coloured pigments, but there is nevertheless an adequate range of colours.

A number of tones in the coloured pigment field (mostly they are the so-called organic pigments) are light-fast in so far as they do not alter colour, i.e. lighten, if white pigment is added to them. If paints are mixed, this can lead to a reduction in the strength of tone, after light has affected it, for example, if a red pigment of the Signal Red tone is lightened by adding yellow and white to make a pink or salmon tone. Such tone-altering effects must be considered when choosing the tones.

The following meet high standards regarding lightfastness, resistance to alkalies and weather:

- Yellow: Iron oxide yellow, Barium yellow, Naples yellow, ochre, terra siena, nickel Titian yellow
- Orange: Chrome orange, cadmium orange
- Red: Iron oxide red, natural or synthetic, chrome red, cadmium red
- Violet: Ultramarine violet, cobalt violet, manganese violet
- Blue: Cobalt blue, manganese blue, phthalocyanin blue, ultramarine blue
- Green: Chrome oxide green, chrome oxide hydrate green, phthalocyanin green, ultramarine green and possibly also mixtures from the pigments mentioned under yellow and blue
- Brown: Iron oxide brown, burnt siena, umber, natural or burnt
- Black: Iron oxide black, manganese black, ivory black, lampblack
- White: (here for the previously mentioned binding agents): Lithopone special product Elkadur, Titanium dioxide Rutil and the blended pigments produced from this, and zinc white. The pigments mentioned here can, with certain exceptions, also be mixed with one another. Additionally there are also multi-coloured pigments (mostly in paste form) available as organic pigment colourings, which frequently give brilliant tones and simultaneously satisfy the requirements.

Which painting techniques are appropriate to which bases?

In view of the confusion which often reigns today regarding the numerous types of coating materials, especially amongst clients, it might be advisable to supplement the previous comments on external painting of render by means of a general survey over the available painting techniques and their appropriateness. At this point it is obvious that only types of material, not trade names, can be mentioned. If one should not be clear as to which type a suggested product belongs to, then a specialist should be consulted. The architect should never, categorically, demand the use of some product without first coming to an agreement with the man who will carry out the painting. His requests regarding the condition of the base should also be borne in mind.

THE USABILITY OF PAINTS ON FACADE AREAS

Paint bases	A	B	C	D	E	F	G	H	I	J
	Lime paint	Noble lime paints	White cement whitewash paints	Silicone paints	Coating for jointless walls of white cement, etc.	Emulsion paints (mostly containing oil) Dispersion paints, synthetic resin renders, dispersion renders	Synthetic latex rubber paints	Linseed oil paints, matt oil paints	Thixotropic, matt laquer paints	
1 Lime renders (mortar group Ia, b)	+	+	+	+	+	+	+	+	+	+
2 Lime renders (mortar group II) Lime cement renders	+	+	+	+	+	+	+	+	+	+
3 Cement renders (mortar group III)	+	+	+	+	+	+	+	+	+	+
4 Simple concrete (no render)	+	+	+	+	+	+	+	+	—	—
5 Exposed concrete	—	/	/	+	/	+	+	+	—	—
6 Wall blocks of gas or expanded concrete	—	—	—	+	+	+	+	+	—	—
7 Absorbent natural stone	—	/	/	+	—	+	+	+	—	—
8 Facing brickwork	—	/	+	+	—	+	+	+	/	/
9 Facing brickwork of engineering bricks, unglazed	—	—	—	—	—	+	+	+	/	/
10 Asbestos cement constructional slabs	—	—	/	+	—	+	+	+	—	—

Key: + equals suitable; / equals suitable with certain limitations, or unsuitable; — equals unsuitable.

Paints F, I and J are, because of their content of dried oils, only usable on renders, concrete and asbestos cement if these surfaces are chemically neutral, i.e. have become completely inert.